All India Oriental Conference
Centenary Celebration Publication Series-35

|| अक्षरपुरुषोत्तमदर्शनकारिकासञ्चयः ||

AKṢARA-PURUṢOTTAMA-DARŚANA-KĀRIKĀ-SAÑCAYA

Explanation, Translation, and Noes

A Students' Guide to Selected Verses from Mahāmahopādhyāya Bhadreshdas Swami's Svāminārāyaṇa-siddhānta-sudhā

Ācārya Brahmasetudas Swami

Chier Editor
Prof. Srinivasa Varkhedi
Vice-Chancellor, KKSU, Ramtek

Editor
Prof. Madhusudan Penna
Director, Research & Publication

Kavikulaguru Kalidas Sanskrit University,
Ramtek
and
New Bharatiya Book Corporation
New Delhi

Title	-	**Akṣara-Puruṣottama-Darśana-Kārikā-Sañcaya**
Authors	-	**Ācārya Brahmasetudas Swami**
Chief Editor	-	**Prof. Srinivasa Varkhedi** Vice-Chancellor, KKSU, Ramtek
Editor	-	**Prof. Madhusudan Penna** Director, Research & Publication
AIOC	-	**Prof. Gautam Patel,** President **Prof. Saroja Bhate,** General Secretary **Prof. G.U. Thite,** Vice President
Editorial Board	-	**Dr. Dinakar Marathe,** KKSU **Dr. Veena Ganu,** Nagpur
Published Year	-	**2020**
Editon	-	**First**
Price	-	**Rs. 495.00**
ISBN	-	**978-81-8315-413-0**
Coverpage	-	**Shri. Umesh Patil**
Published by	-	**Kulasachiva, Kavikulaguru Kalidas Sanskrit University, Ramtek** & **New Bharatiya Book Corporation** 208, IInd Floor, Prakash Deep Building 4735/22, Ansari Road, Daryaganj, New Delhi-110002 Phone : 23280214, 23280209

Printer - S. K. Offset, New Delhi

PREFACE

It is indeed a matter of great pleasure and pride for Kavikulaguru Kalidas Sanskrit University, Ramtek to have this rarest opportunity of hosting the 50th session of All India Oriental Conference at Nagpur. This AIOC-50th session at Nagpur will be forever remembered by all as the year 2019 also happens to be the year of Centenary Celebration of AIOC. The premier objective with which the great scholars of yester years had contemplated and established this national academic event called All India Oriental Conference has been achieved through these years with scores of young scholars contributing significantly to the treasure house of knowledge through their valuable research work.

The research of yore and of the present should be properly recorded so as to make it easily available to all lovers of knowledge and wisdom in the years to come. With this objective, we have contemplated to commemorate the 100th year of this grand event of 50th session of AIOC by way of publishing 100 monographs on different subjects in four languages viz., Sanskrit, Hindi, Marathi and English. It is no doubt a herculean task but still worth of it, for the reason that these 100 monographs will inspire many young scholars to take upon a fresh study and research of the oriental subjects with more vigour and zeal.

The AIOC Centenary Publication Series includes wide variety of subjects like Literature, Language, Veda, Indian Philosophy, Sanskrit Grammar, Law, Children Literature, Yoga, Astronomy and Astrology, Ayurveda, Pali, Prakrit, Jain, Buddhism, Education, Library Science, Poetics, Aesthetics, and Indology. It also includes reprint of some rare texts of academic importance which have gone out of print are not easily available. We wish to mark this centenary celebrations with this series that connects the glory of the past and aspirations of future. I place on record my sincere gratitude to all the authors of these monographs who have kindly contributed to the richness of this series.

I am confident that the books published in these series will definitely inspire the lovers of Oriental Learning in general and of Sanskrit Language and Literature in particular.

On this occasion, we have published a memorable book of all the speeches of Section-Presidents of all previous sessions of AIOC. It is indeed a very capacious addition to any collection. I with all respect thank two eminent scholars of our times - Prof. Gautam Patel, President and Prof. Saroja Bhate, General Secretary, the torch bearers of AIOC who have not only encouraged us in this venture but also made all efforts to provide these valuable historical speeches for us. I thank all executive members of AIOC and my colleagues of the varsity for making this event a grand success. My words fall short in describing the painstaking efforts and scholarly commitment of my esteemed colleague Prof. Madhusudan Penna, local secretary of this session in bringing out this series.

I also take this opportunity to profusely thank Shri. Subhash Jain and Shri Deepak Jain, the proprietors of New Bharatiya Book Corporation, New Delhi for their enthusiastic approach and timely work with all precision and grace.

Let us all sanctify ourselves in the eternal flow of wisdom by reading these books and recommending these to others also!

सरस्वती श्रुतिमहती महीयताम्

Ramtek
10th January 2020

Prof. Srinivasa Varakhedi
Vice Chancellor, KKSU

Kavikulaguru Kalidas Sanskrit University
All India Oriental Conference

100th Year 50th Session
10th-12th January, 2020

Chief Patron
Hon'ble Nitin Gadkari
Minister of Road, Transport & Highways of India

Patron
Prof. Srinivasa Varakhedi
Vice Chancellor, KKSU, Ramtek

AIOC President
Prof. Gautam Patel
Chairman, Sanskrit Seva Samiti, Ahmedabad.

AIOC General Secretary
Prof. Saroja Bhate
Professor of Sanskrit (Retd.), Pune University, Pune

AIOC Local Secretary
Prof. Penna Madhusudan
Dean, KKSU, Ramtek

Additional Local Secretary
Dr. Harekrishna Agasti
Dr. Kalapini Agasti
Dr. Dinakar Marathe
Dr. Parag Joshi

Organising Committee

Prof. C.G. Vijayakumar, Registrar (I/c) & Dean, KKSU, Ramtek
Prof. Nanda Puri, Dean, KKSU, Ramtek
Prof. Krishnakumar Pandey, Dean, KKSU, Ramtek
Prof. Laita Chandratre, Dean, KKSU, Ramtek
Dr. Ramachandra Joshi, Finance Officer, KKSU, Ramtek
Dr. Umesh Shivahare, Controller of Examination, KKSU, Ramtek
Dr. Dipak Kapade, Librarian, KKSU, Ramtek
Dr. Renuka Bokare, PRO, KKSU, Ramtek
Shri. Rajivranjan Mishra, Technical Head, KKSU, Ramtek
Shri. Pravin Kalambe, Security Officer, KKSU, Ramtek

Reception Committee

Prof. Srinivasa Varakhedi, Chairperson Reception Committee & VC, KKSU
Parampujya Govindagiri Swamiji, Rishikesh
Prof. P.T. Chande, Former VC, KKSU
Prof. Uma Vaidya, Former VC, KKSU
Prof. Vijendra Kumar, VC, National Law University, Nagpur
Prof. Rajnish Shukla, VC, National Hindi University, Wardha
Prof. Vinayak Kane, VC, RTM Nagpur University, Nagpur
Shri. Krupal Tumane, Member of Parliament
Shri. Girishji Vyas, Member of Legislative Council
Shri. Chandrashekhar Bawankule, Guardian Minister, Nagpur
Prof. Vishram Jamdar, Director, VNIT, Nagpur
Dr. Bhushankumar Upadhyay, Commissioner of Police, Nagpur
Shri. Vijay Phanshikar, Editor, The Hitavada, Nagpur
Shri. Rajkumar Tirpude, Tirpude Group of Insitutions, Nagpur
Shri. Mohabbat Singh, Tuli International, Nagpur.
Shri. Chandragupta Varnekar, Principal Retd., Nagpur
Shri. Suresh Sharma, Baidyanath, Nagpur
Shri. Prabhakar Rao Mundle, Dharampeth Educational Institutions, Nagpur

Executive Committee

Prof. G. U. Thite,
Vice President

Dr. Brijeshkumar Shukla,
Treasurer

Members

Dr. Rajni Satish Chandra Jha
Prof. Shukla Ramakant
Dr. Behera Ranjit
Dr. Meena Shukla
Dr. Nirmala Kulkarni
Dr. Roy Gauri Nath
Dr. Tripathi Uma Rani
Dr. Pushpa Jha
Dr. Basu Ratna

Dr. Mithilesh Kumar
Prof. Singh Prasoon Dutta
Shri. Mishra Arun Ranjan
Dr. Mishra Baidyanath
Dr. Tripathi Rajendra Rasraj
Shri. Harshdev Madhav
Dr. Kamdev Jha
Dr. Parinita Deshpande
Dr. Jha Udayanath (Ashok)

Parabrahman Puruṣottama Swaminarayan (1781-1830 CE) (right) and Akṣarabrahman Gunatitanand Swami '1785-1867 CE) (left), the focal points of the Akṣara-Puruṣottama Darśana.
This image, which was gifted to Pramukh Swami Maharaj in 1977, is embellished with the fragment of a cloth that once belonged Bhagwan Swaminarayan. Pramukh Swami Maharaj daily offered worship to this image and its accompanying relic as part of his morning puja ritual.

Source: Courtesy of the BAPS Swaminarayan Sanstha.

On the Occasion of Pramukh Swami Maharaj's Centenary Celebrations...

This Work is Dedicated to...

Parabrahman Puruṣottama Swaminarayan,
who revealed the knowledge of
the Akṣara-Puruṣottama Darśana.

Shastriji Maharaj, who gave the Darśana
a concrete form
and an appropriate name.

Pramukh Swami Maharaj, who inspired
the writing of the Svāminārāyaṇa-bhāṣyam
and the Svāminārāyaṇa-siddhānta-sudhā.

Mahant Swami Maharaj, who inspired
the creation of this work.

Foreword

Indian philosophy has been blessed with the advent of various schools of thought over the ages. Most recently, the Vedānta school has seen the introduction of a significant new stream, Parabrahman Swaminarayan's Akṣara-Puruṣottama Darśana. Many of India's foremost scholars have lauded this new darśana as a unique and authentic Vedantic school. They have also praised Mahāmahopādhyāya Bhadreshdas Swami's comprehensive, Saṃskṛta texts elucidating this philosophy, the *Prasthānatrayī-svāminārāyaṇa-bhāṣyam* (2009-12) and the *Svāminārāyaṇa-siddhānta-sudhā* (2017), as seminal contributions to the Vedāntic heritage.

I, too, have read Bhadreshdas Swami's texts myself and have been overwhelmed to see their unique principles, novel reflections, exceptional literary style, and lucid language. Certainly, Bhadreshdas Swami has revived the centuries-old bhāṣya and vāda-grantha tradition by producing these magnanimous works.

Along with this acceptance and praise, however, a need has arisen for these texts to be presentable in a format that can be accessed widely, particularly by beginners. The *Svāminārāyaṇa-siddhānta-sudhā* appeared to me as the best place to start. Indeed, this literary masterpiece thoroughly establishes the Akṣara-Puruṣottama Darśana's primary tenets in the classical style of polemics, while also summarising these principles through 548 concise yet engaging verses. I felt that producing a work that deconstructs the most important of these verses would be a noteworthy academic contribution.

I approached Bhadreshdas Swami with my idea two years ago. Bhadreshdas Swami readily agreed and asked Acharya Brahmasetudas Swami to undertake this task. Thereafter, Bhadreshdas Swami, Brahmasetudas Swami, and I worked together to envision this project.

Ācārya Brahmasetudas Swami has traditionally studied Nyāya, Vyākaraṇa, and the Akṣara-Puruṣottama Darśana's Saṃskṛta and vernacular texts for the past fifteen years. Moreover, he has closely worked with Bhadreshdas Swami throughout this time. I have also had the opportunity to engage with him over the past several years and can testify to his academic rigour. As an expert scholar and an authority in the field of the Akṣara-Puruṣottama Darśana, he is uniquely positioned to undertake this project.

I am happy to see that this endeavour has come to fruition in the form of the present work. This text will indeed be a useful addition to university courses on Indian philosophy and the Akṣara-Puruṣottama Darśana.

I express my sincere gratitude to Bhadreshdas Swami and Brahmasetudas Swami. I genuinely hope to see more such scholarship produced in the coming years. I pray to Bhagwan Swaminarayan that he blesses us so that we may further understand his visionary teachings and help others do the same.

Dr Rabindra Kumar Panda
Professor and Former Head
Dept. of Sanskrit, Pali & Prakrit
Faculty of Arts, The Maharaja Sayajirao University

Teacher's Guide

As a teacher of Nyāya, Vyākaraṇa, and the Akṣara-Puruṣottama Darśana, I have come to realise that Indian philosophy's conversations can be enriching and edifying on the one hand, yet voluminous and difficult to navigate on the other hand. Those wishing to learn, nonetheless, often address this conundrum by forgoing primary texts and instead relying on secondary, summary texts.

This book, one of a series of forthcoming works, attempts to make one of the Akṣara-Puruṣottama Darśana's crucial primary texts accessible to students. It does so by providing translations and other pedagogical tools that explicate some of the most important passages of the *Svāminārāyaṇa-siddhānta-sudhā*, the Akṣara-Puruṣottama Darśana's vāda-grantha. What follows is a brief overview of this volume and a guide to several of its features.

Overview

This text is made up of nine chapters that are coterminous with the chapters of the *Svāminārāyaṇa-siddhānta-sudhā*. Each chapter is known as a 'dhārā'. The term 'sudhā' literally refers to ambrosia or amrita, whereas 'dhārā' indicates a stream. The analogy here thus signifies that the *Siddhānta-sudhā's* chapters constitute streams of immortalising nectar. By providing knowledge of the Divine, these dhārās lead us towards enlightenment, ultimate liberation, and eternal bliss.

Below is an outline of this work's chapters:

1. The Maṅgala-dhārā – Presents the author's obeisance to Swaminarayan, who established the Akṣara-Puruṣottama Darśana, and the lineage of Akṣarabrahman gurus, who have fostered the darśana.

2. The Akṣarabrahma-dhārā – Explores the soteriological significance, form, and nature of the entity of Akṣarabrahman; also discusses Akṣarabrahman's four forms.

3. The Parabrahma-dhārā – Considers the form and attributes of God, also known as Puruṣottama; also examines the nature of Puruṣottama's perennial manifestation on earth.

4. The Pramāṇa-dhārā – Explains knowledge and the means of acquiring it.

5. The Jīva-dhārā – Explicates the form and nature of the ātman, or the individual soul.

6. The Īśvara-dhārā – Considers the form and nature of the īśvara, a category of sentient beings that are responsible for creation, sustenance, and dissolution.

7. The Māyā-dhārā – Presents māyā as the entity that prevents beings from attaining experiential knowledge; also explores how people can overcome māyā and attain liberation.

8. The Sādhana-dhārā – Explains spiritual praxis, chief of which is identifying with Akṣarabrahman and worshipping Parabrahman.

9. The Phala-dhārā – Describes the two types of liberation acquired by one who successfully practices the endeavours described in the previous chapter.

The text ends by again praising Swaminarayan and the lineage of Akṣarabrahman gurus and also extolling the countless of devotees who daily live, experience, and celebrate the Akṣara-Puruṣottama Darśana.

How to Use this Book

It is essential to make a note of this work's audience before moving forth. Indeed, the Akṣara-Puruṣottama Darśana has garnered attention from students and scholars around the world, including those who adhere to either traditional or modern modes of scholarship. This work attempts to address the needs of both audiences with particular attention towards those who are novitiates to the Akṣara-Puruṣottama Darśana and the Saṃskṛta language.

The work thus begins with the 'Siddhānta-patram', a philosophical document written in 2008 by Pramukh Swami Maharaj, Swaminarayan's fifth successor and the inspirer of the *Svāminārāyaṇa-bhāṣyam* and *Siddhānta-sudhā*. The 'Siddhānta-patram' outlines the Akṣara-Puruṣottama Darśana's key principles in prose, providing context for the reader to understand the verses presented in this work.

Thereafter, each of this book's nine chapters is preceded by an introduction that maps the author's key arguments and sheds light on the way the overall work develops through each subsequent chapter.

The verses encompassed in this book are each presented with the following components:

1. The text of the original, selected verses appears in both Devanāgari and transliterated, Roman script.
2. Padacchedas are presented in Devanāgari. This is done by removing sandhis, or elisions resulting from phonetic morphology, and is meant to help readers clearly identify the terms that comprise each verse.

3. Charts are given to offer each verse's anvaya or reordering according to Saṃskṛta grammatical sequence. These charts also include word-by-word (and generally literal) English translations of each component of the verse in question.

4. English translations of the verses in their entirety are lastly given. These translations more often accord to English grammatical style and standards and attempt to shed light on implied meaning, rather than adhering to literal translation. This convention is meant to ease readability and understanding of the verses presented.

Often, verses are accompanied by footnotes that link individual verses or explore critical ideas not presented in the text. While these footnotes are far from exhaustive, they provide avenues for further inquiry and a more holistic understanding of the principles presented within each verse.

Conventions of Translation and Transliteration

Translation is always a difficult task, as it involves transferring ideas not just from one language to another but from one cultural realm to another. Inevitably, pieces of the original are always lost in the process. The translator's task is to minimise such loss but also to render an accessible text. Accordingly, most of the original Saṃskṛta in this work has been translated into English. Nontheless, technical terms have often not been used in translation, keeping in mind that this text is targeted towards beginners.

At the same time, terms that are essential to the Akṣara-Puruṣottama Darśana or the Vedānta tradition and are commonly used in their texts have often been left untranslated. Such terms have generally been treated in one of two ways: 1) if left untranslated, they are accompanied by a footnote at first instance and a glossary entry; 2) if translated, they are often used concurrently or interchangeably with their Saṃskṛta counterparts.

Diacritics have been included in all Saṃskṛta-based, common nouns. Saṃskṛta-based, proper nouns that name locations do not employ diacritics. The names of well-known people are treated similarly, although their first mentions are accompanied by diacritical representation in parenthesis. Transliterations appear according to the standards of the International Alphabet of Sanskrit Transliteration, or IAST.

Italics have not been used anywhere for Saṃskṛta-based, common nouns in order to enhance readability. Italics have been employed for the titles of texts; however, those texts that the Akṣara-Puruṣottama Darśana considers to be of the śruti (revelatory) category are not italicised.

Words added to the translations that appear in charts have been put in either brackets or parenthesis. Brackets signify words that have been added to complete a sentence or thought, whereas parentheses signify those that have been added for explanation.

Along with contemporary referencing standards, this book also employs traditional referencing, as classical scholars generally prefer this method and as page numbers vary amongst the numerous editions of the primary sources cited here.

Siddhanta-Patram

Pramukh Swami Maharaj

(Śāstrī Nārāyaṇasvarūpadāsa)[1]

The five entities – jīva, īśvara, māyā, Brahman (Brahma) and Parabrahman (Parabrahman) – are eternal, existent and forever ontologically distinct.

Parabrahman

Parabrahman Puruṣottamanārāyaṇa, who is the sovereign of Akṣara, is eternal, supreme, always divine, ever with a form, faultless, above māyā, one and unparalleled, and a cetana (sentient) entity.

Within his divine Akṣaradhāman, he is seated on a divine throne in his eternally divine, lustrous and teenage human form complete with two arms and all other features. He (Parabrahman) is worshipped with dāsabhāva (wilful servitude) by the mūrtimān (personal) form of Akṣarabrahman and infinite muktas (released jīvātmans and īśvarātmans). These muktas have attained a brāhmitanu and have attained likeness with Akṣarabrahman. Parabrahman is eternally and innately re-

1 This letter, written by Pramukh Swami Maharaj, outlines Akṣara-Puruṣottama Darśana. It is based on this letter that Sadhu Bhadreshdas wrote the *Svāminārāyaṇa-siddhānta-sudhā*.

plete with infinite liberating virtues and devoid of the qualities of māyā. He is without deficiency, forever possesses all powers, is all-knowing, and the all-doer. He is the material and efficient cause of all creation. He, while residing in his divine Akṣaradhāman in his vyatireka (particular) form, pervades and is the support of infinite brahmāṇḍas (universes) in his anvaya (all-pervasive) form as their antaryāmin. He is always infinitely more powerful than jīvas, īśvaras, māyā, akṣara muktas and Akṣarabrahman and is their independent controller, inspirer and śarīrin (embodier). By his own wish, he is the giver of the fruits of the actions of all the jīvas and īśvaras, and is the inspirer of their ability to will, to know and to do.

Parabrahman Puruṣottamanārāyaṇa, who is imperceptible by māyic (worldly) indriyas (senses) and antaḥkaraṇa (inner faculties), while remaining in Akṣaradhāman, by his own divine wish and out of compassion, for the ultimate liberation of infinite jīvas and īśvaras, and to fulfil the wishes of his devotees, manifests with all his divine virtues, powers, etc., in perceptible human form in each brahmāṇḍa and becomes visible to all.

That manifest form of Parabrahman Paramātman is Sahajanand Swami Maharaj – Shri Swaminarayan Bhagwan (Sahajānanda Svāmī Mahārāja – Śrī Svāminārāyaṇa Bhagavān). Only he is the absolute focus of worship for us all. He always remains entirely manifest in his anvaya form through the Akṣarabrahman guru to forever continue the upāsanā (worshipful service) of his manifest form even after his disappearance (leaving of his human body).

He (Parabrahman) is the cause of all avatāras; he is the avatārin and the sovereign of them all. An avatāra occurs when he (Parabrahman) pervades a jīva or īśvara with the wish to fulfil a task. The cetanas (beings) of each of these avatāras are ontologically and inherently distinct from one another.

Akṣarabrahman

Akṣarabrahman is distinct from Parabrahman, and like Parabrahman it is eternal, one, beyond the three guṇas (qualities), a cetana (sentient) entity, and forever divine. Replete with infinite liberating virtues and devoid of all māyic qualities, it is eternally without faults. This Akṣarabrahman's form, qualities, powers, etc. are dependent only to Parabrahman. By Parabrahman's eternal wish, it is the cause, support, pervader, controller and śarīrin of all creation, which is jaḍacidātmaka .

Although Akṣarabrahman is metaphysically one entity, it serves in different ways through four forms.

In its cidākāśa form, Akṣarabrahman pervades within and outside infinite brahmāṇḍas and upholds them.

As an abode (Akṣaradhāman), Akṣarabrahman is the divine abode of 1) Parabrahman; 2) the mūrtimān form of Akṣarabrahman, who is in his (Parabrahman's) service; and 3) infinite akṣara muktas (released jīvātmans and īśvarātmans). There is only one such Akṣaradhāman. It is eternal and forever beyond the three guṇas. Only muktas, who have attained qualitative similarity to Akṣarabrahman, are able to enter it.

In that same Akṣaradhāman, Akṣarabrahman's form as the personal attendant has, like Parabrahman, a divine human form complete with two arms and all other features. As the ideal for akṣara muktas, he forever remains engrossed in Parabrahman's service.

That very Akṣarabrahman manifests in human form, in each brahmāṇḍa along with Parabrahman, as the guru, who is the complete and uninterrupted vessel of Parabrahman. Akṣara can make bound jīvas and īśvaras of the world brahmarūpa, have them attain uttama nirvikalpa niścaya (the greatest unwavering conviction) of Parabrahman, attain ultimate liberation, and forever experience the manifest presence of Paramātman through his (Akṣara's) divine association. He protects the traditions of the sampradāya and causes all to experience the supreme bliss. Gunatitanand Swami (Guṇātītānanda Svāmī), Bhagatji Maharaj (Bhagatajī Mahārāja), Shastriji Maharaj (Shastriji Mahārāja) and Yogiji Maharaj (Yogījī Mahārāja) have appeared in this succession of guṇātīta Akṣarabrahman gurus. This succession will continue uninterruptedly. At any given time, the path of ultimate liberation remains open through only one guru.

Māyā

Māyā is composed of the three guṇas, eternally changing, jaḍa, a material cause of the creation of infinite brahmāṇḍas, and Paramātman's diverse, mysterious power. As the cause of ego and attachment of jīvas and of īśvaras, this very māyā has been the cause of their births and deaths since eternity. Akṣarabrahman and Parabrahman are forever entirely untainted by, beyond, and the śarīrin of this māyā.

Īśvara

An īśvara is an eternal cetana (sentient) entity distinct from Parabrahman, Akṣarabrahman and jīvas. Despite being extremely powerless when compared to Akṣarabrahman and Parabrahman; these īśvaras bear greater power and knowledge than jīvas. Through his wish, Paramātman inspires them to perform tasks of creation, etc. of the brahmāṇḍas. Like the jīvas, these īśvaras are countless in number, infinitesimal (extremely small), indivisible, and possess other such qualities. They are jñānasvarūpa, jñātā (those who know), and eternally bound by māyā. They perform righteous and unrighteous karmas (actions) and experience the fruits of those actions.

Pradhāna Puruṣa, Virāt Puruṣa, the deities of their senses (indriyas) and the inner faculties (antaḥkaraṇa) are all beings of the īśvara category; and these īśvaras are ontologically and inherently distinct from one another.

Jīva

The jīva is an eternal, cetana (sentient) entity ontologically distinct from Parabrahman, Akṣarabrahman, and īśvaras. These jīvas are countless, infinitesimal (extremely small), indivisible, and possess other such qualities. They are jñānasvarūpa, jñātā (those who know), and eternally bound by māyā. They perform righteous and unrighteous karmas (actions) and experience the fruits of those actions.

Spiritual Endeavour And Its Benefits

To attain ultimate liberation, mumukṣus (spiritual aspirants) should have firm love for Parabrahman Puruṣottama Bhagavān Swaminarayan and the present Akṣarabrahman guru, through whom Parabrahman is fully and continuously manifest, by having nirdoṣa buddhi in them, a feeling of the highest divinity in them, and upon meeting them, conviction in having met the present form of Parabrahman. They should greatly please them by firmly associating with them through thought, word and deed.

Aspirant jīvas and īśvaras who endeavour in this way, through Parabrahman's grace, having attained ekāntika dharma and having become brahmarūpa, that is, having attained similarity to Akṣarabrahman, acquire the highest devotion to Parabrahman. All their miseries and faults are forever destroyed, and they experience the supreme bliss of Paramātman while alive. By Paramātman's wish, such a brahmarūpa devotee, upon leaving the body, attains Paramātman's Akṣaradhāman through the arcimārga. There, having attained a brāhmic-body, the devotee forever enjoys divine bliss while offering, with dāsabhāva, service in the form of performing darśana of Parabrahman, the

Lord of Akṣaradhāman.

The Meaning Behind Akṣarapuruṣottama Upāsanā

Akṣarapuruṣottama upāsanā is not the upāsanā of two entities – Akṣara and Puruṣottama; but it refers to offering upāsanā to Puruṣottama having become akṣararūpa – in other words, to offer upāsanā to Parabrahman having become brahmarūpa. When Parabrahman, who travels (manifests) in human form, returns to his abode, he absorbs the powers of the Brahmasvarūpa guru and himself travels (remains manifest on earth) through him. Therefore, an aspirant who associates with the manifest guru is, in fact, offering upāsanā only to one Paramātmā.

The meaning of the Swaminarayan mahāmantra is incorporated in this meaning of Akṣara-Puruṣottama upāsanā: that is, to become svāmirūpa - akṣararūpa, and offer devotion – upāsanā with dāsabhāva to Nārāyaṇa - Parabrahman Puruṣottama Nārāyaṇa.

Conclusion

In this way, these philosophical principles are Vedic, eternal, revealed by Shriji Maharaj (Śrījī Mahārāja, i.e. Svāminārāyaṇa), and propagated by the lineage of guṇātīta gurus.

Jay Swaminarayan from Shastri Narayanswarupdas (Śāstrī Nārāyaṇasvarūpadāsa)

Guru Pūrṇimā, Saṃvata 2064 (18 July 2008), Bochasan

Table of Contents

Chapter 1 : Maṅgala-dhārā 1

1.1 Introduction 1

1.2 Benediction 3

1.3 Akṣara-Puruṣottama Vandanā 6

1.4 Yajñapuruṣa-stava 7

1.5 Nārāyaṇasvarūpa-abhidhyāna 17

1.6 Abhyarthanā 29

1.7 The Swaminarayan Mantra's Significance 31

1.8 The Five Eternal Entities 33

Chapter 2 : Akṣarabrahma-dhārā 39

2.1 Introduction 39

2.2 Benediction 41

2.3 Novelty 43

2.4 Akṣarabrahman's Soteriological Significance 45

2.5 An Etymological Analysis 46

2.6 Akṣarabrahman's Virtues & Figure 49

2.7 One Entity with Four Forms 52

2.8 Akṣarabrahman's Prevalence in the Śāstras 67

Chapter 3 : Parabrahma-dhārā 69

3.1 Introduction 69

3.2 Benediction 71
3.3 Parabrahman's Divine Virtues & Figure 72
3.4 Manifestation as Swaminarayan 79
3.5 Premise for Creation 83
3.6 Parabrahman's Sacred Form 84
3.7 Pre-Eminence and Perennial Manifestation 89
3.8 Inherent Divinity 94
Chapter 4 : Pramāṇa-dhārā 97
4.1 Introduction 97
4.2 Benediction 99
4.3 Knowledge 102
4.4 Perception 105
4.5 Inference 109
4.6 Verbal Testimony 113
4.7 The Preeminence of the Knowledge Event 126
4.8 Erroneous Knowledge 128
Chapter 5 : Māyā-dhārā 133
5.1 Introduction 133
5.2 Benediction 134
5.3 Māyā's Nature & Form 135
5.4 Māyā's Role in Creation and Transmigration 136
5.5 Māyā's Various Names 138
5.6 Māyā's Three Qualities 139
5.7 Overcoming Māyā 140
Chapter 6 : Jīva-dhārā 143
6.1 Introduction 143
6.2 Benediction 145
6.3 An Etymological Analysis 146

6.4 The Jīva's Three Bodies & States of Being 147
6.5 How Paramātman Empowers the Jīva 151
6.6 The Jīva's Inherent Nature 152
Chapter 7 : Īśvara-dhārā 157
7.1 Introduction 157
7.2 An Etymological Analysis 158
7.3 The Īśvara's Nature & Form 159
7.4 The Īśvara's Three Bodies & States of Being 161
Chapter 8 : Sādhana-dhārā 165
8.1 Introduction 165
8.2 Benediction 167
8.3 Attaining Oneness with Akṣarabrahman 170
8.4 Ekāntika Dharma 175
8.5 Dharma 179
8.6 Jñāna 182
8.7 Vairāgya 183
8.8 Bhakti 184
8.9 Spiritual Endeavour 188
Chapter 9 : Phala-dhārā 195
9.1 Introduction 195
9.2 Benediction 197
9.3 Defining Liberation 198
9.4 Videha-mukti 201
9.5 The Significance of these Verses 208
Concluding Verses & Benediction 210
Appendix : Mahāmahopādhyāya Bhadreshdas Swami 217
Index of Verses 219
Glossary 227

Chapter 1

Maṅgala-dhārā

1.1 Introduction

Saṃskṛta texts often begin with benedictions aimed at invoking blessings for the successful completion of the work being composed. Such benediction is known as the maṅgalācaraṇa (literally, 'auspicious act'). In this tradition, the *Svāminārāyaṇa-siddhānta-sudhā*'s first chapter, adequately named the 'Maṅgala-dhārā', commences with prayers to Parabrahman Puruṣottama Bhagwan Swaminarayan (Bhagavān Svāminārāyaṇa), the founder of the Akṣara-Puruṣottama Darśana. These prayers recall Bhagwan Swaminarayan's various names and recount his life and auspicious works – his inspiring journey as a child yogī, establishment and nourishment of the Swaminarayan fellowship, and promise to stay forever present on earth through a lineage of brahmasvarūpa gurus.[1]

This chapter then offers obeisance to Akṣara and Puruṣottama, the entities that form the epicentre of the Akṣara-Puruṣottama Darśana. Thereafter, it presents the 'Yajñapuruṣa-stava'. This section contains the author's homage to Brahmasvarūpa

---

1 This lineage includes Akṣarabrahman Gunatitanand Swami (1785-1863 CE), Brahmasvarūpa Bhagatji Maharaj (1829-98 CE), Brahmasvarūpa Shastriji Maharaj (1865-1951 CE), Brahmasvarūpa Yogiji Maharaj (1892-1971 CE), Brahmasvarūpa Pramukh Swami Maharaj (1921-2016 CE), and Pragaṭa Brahmasvarūpa Mahant Swami Maharaj (b.1933 CE).

Shastriji Maharaj (Śāstrijī Mahārāja), the third successor in the lineage of Akṣarabrahman gurus. Shastriji Maharaj gave name and form to Bhagwan Swaminarayan's philosophy by entitling it 'the Akṣara-Puruṣottama Darśana' and consecrated the mūrtis of Akṣara and Puruṣottama in majestic, stone mandiras. The Yajñapuruṣa-stava, specifically, recounts Shastriji Maharaj's erudition, courage, and tireless efforts to establish and spread the Akṣara-Puruṣottama Darśana. It also recalls his selection of Brahmasvarūpa Yogiji Maharaj (Yogijī Mahārāja) and Brahmasvarūpa Pramukh Swami Maharaj (Pramukha Svāmī Mahārāja) as his successors.

Through the next section, the 'Nārāyaṇasvarūpa-abhidhyāna', the author bows to his guru, Brahmasvarūpa Pramukh Swami Maharaj, who inspired the creation of the *Svāminārāyaṇa-siddhānta-sudhā*. This benediction describes Pramukh Swami Maharaj as a sthitaprajña yogī, guṇātīta, and Paramātman's dearest. It also extolls him as being the only person who can help people achieve absolute conviction in Paramātman.

Thereafter, via the 'Abhyarthanā', the author bows to Pramukh Swami Maharaj's successor, Mahant Swami Maharaj (Mahanta Svāmī Mahārāja), the manifest, Akṣarabrahman guru.

The 'Maṅgala-dhārā' concludes with an overview of the *Svāminārāyaṇa-siddhānta-sudhā*. This sketch includes an explanation of the Swaminarayan mantra, which plays an essential role in prayer in the Akṣara-Puruṣottama Darśana. It also enumerates the five eternal entities, whose knowledge leads to the perfection of brahmavidyā. Lastly, the author writes that the *Svāminārāyaṇa-siddhānta-sudhā* is not an independent creation but is merely a joyful recollection of the truths presented in the 'Siddhānta-patram', the philosophical document that was written by Pramukh Swami Maharaj in 2008 (see front matter).

1.2 Benediction

The author begins with an invocation to his iṣṭadeva, Bhagwan Swaminarayan, wherein he evokes Swaminarayan by his different names.

मङ्गलं सहजानन्दः श्रीहरिर्मङ्गलं शुभम्।
मङ्गलं नीलकण्ठो हि स्वामिनारायणः सदा॥ १॥

maṅgalaṃ sahajānandaḥ śrīharirmaṅgalaṃ śubham,
maṅgalaṃ nīlakaṇṭho hi svāminārāyaṇaḥ sadā.

पदच्छेदः - मङ्गलम्, सहजानन्दः, श्रीहरिः, मङ्गलम्, शुभम्, मङ्गलम्, नीलकण्ठः, हि, स्वामिनारायणः, सदा॥

अन्वयः

सहजानन्दः - Sahajanand (Sahajānanda)

मङ्गलम् - auspicious

श्रीहरिः - Shri Hari (Śrī Hari)

मङ्गलम् - auspicious

शुभम् - benevolent

मङ्गलम् - auspicious

नीलकण्ठः - Neelkanth (Nīlakaṇṭha)

हि - indeed

स्वामिनारायणः - Swaminarayan

सदा - ever

(मङ्गलम्) - auspicious

Sahajanand is auspicious. Shri Hari, certainly, is auspicious and benevolent. Neelkanth is auspicious. Swaminarayan is forever auspicious, indeed. (1)

आदौ भक्त्यङ्गजन्मा गहनवनगतिर्नीलकण्ठस्वरूपे
सिद्धान्तस्थापनार्थं स्थितिमतिदयया सम्प्रदायप्रतिष्ठाम्।
कृत्वा यागान् अहिंसान् सहजसुखकरान् त्यागिनो मन्दिराणि
प्राकट्यं ब्रह्मणि स्वं सकलजनहिते स्थापयन् धाम यातः ॥ २ ॥

ādau bhaktyaṅgajanmā gahanavanagatirnīlakaṇṭhasvarūpe,
siddhāntasthāpanārthaṃ sthitimatidayayā sampradāyapratiṣṭhām.
kṛtvā yāgān ahiṃsān sahajasukhakarān tyāgino mandirāṇi,
prākaṭyaṃ brahmaṇi svaṃ sakalajanahite sthāpayan dhāma yātaḥ.

<u>पदच्छेदः</u> - आदौ, भक्त्यङ्गजन्मा, गहनवनगतिः, नीलकण्ठस्वरूपे, सिद्धान्तस्थापनार्थम् स्थितिम्, अतिदयया, सम्प्रदायप्रतिष्ठाम्, कृत्वा, यागान्, अहिंसान्, सहजसुखकरान्, त्यागिनः, मन्दिराणि, प्राकट्यम्, ब्रह्मणि, स्वम्, सकलजनहिते, स्थापयन्, धाम, यातः ॥

<u>अन्वयः</u>

आदौ - at first

भक्त्यङ्गजन्मा - he who was born of Bhakti

नीलकण्ठस्वरूपे - in the form of Neelkanth

गहनवनगतिः - he who travelled through dense forests

स्थितिम् (कृत्वा) - having stopped his travels

अतिदयया - compassionately

सिद्धान्तस्थापनार्थम् - to establish his philosophical principles

सम्प्रदायप्रतिष्ठाम् (कृत्वा) - having established the sampradāya

सहजसुखकरान् - those that gracefully imparted peace

अहिंसान् - non-violent

यागान् - yajñas

त्यागिनः - sādhus

मन्दिराणि - mandiras

कृत्वा - having created

सकलजनहिते - for the welfare of all

स्वम् - his own

प्राकट्यम् - manifestation

ब्रह्मणि - in Akṣarabrahman

स्थापयन् - establishing

धाम - the divine abode

यातः - went to

Swaminarayan, who was born of Bhakti,[2] travelled through dense forests in the form of Neelkanth. He ended his travels and compassionately founded a sampradāya to establish his philosophical principles. Thereafter, he performed non-violent yajñas, created mandiras, and initiated sādhus, all of which imparted peace. He then returned to his divine abode, having established his continuing manifestation through Akṣarabrahman[3] for the welfare of all. (2)

2 Bhagwan Swaminarayan was born to Bhaktidevī and Dharmadeva Pāṇḍe on 3 April 1781 (Dave, Bhagavān Śrī Svāminārāyaṇa, Vol.1, 22). In the present verse, the author recalls Swaminarayan's divine birth by referring to him as the son of Bhakti.

3 'Akṣara', 'Brahman', and 'Akṣarabrahman' are synonymous terms, as is established in the *Svāminārāyaṇa-siddhānta-sudhā* through several śāstric references (Bhadreshdas 19). To prevent confusion, however, all references to any of these terms are translated here as 'Akṣarabrahman'.

1.3 Akṣara-Puruṣottama Vandanā

The author now bows to Akṣara and Puruṣottama while also revealing the implicit meaning of the word Swaminarayan.

स्वामिनारायणं नौमि ह्यक्षरपुरुषोत्तमम्।
स्वामिनारायणौ नौमि ह्यक्षरपुरुषोत्तमौ ॥ ३ ॥

svāminārāyaṇaṃ naumi hyakṣarapuruṣottamam,
svāminārāyaṇau naumi hyakṣarapuruṣottamau.

पदच्छेदः - स्वामिनारायणम्, नौमि, हि, अक्षरपुरुषोत्तमम्, स्वामिनारायणौ, नौमि, हि, अक्षरपुरुषोत्तमौ ॥

अन्वयः

स्वामिनारायणम् - to Nārāyaṇa along with Svāmī

अक्षरपुरुषोत्तमम् - to Puruṣottama along with Svāmī

हि - indeed

नौमि - I bow

स्वामिनारायणौ - to Svāmī and Nārāyaṇa

हि - indeed

अक्षरपुरुषोत्तमौ - to Akṣara and Puruṣottama

नौमि - I bow

I bow to Nārāyaṇa along with Svāmī, that is, Puruṣottama along with Akṣara. I bow to Svāmī and Nārāyaṇa, that is, Akṣara and Puruṣottama. (3)

1.4 Yajñapuruṣa-stava

Brahmasvarūpa Shastriji Maharaj, also known as Yagnapurushdas (Yajñapuruṣadāsa), was Swaminarayan's third successor. He coined Swaminarayan's doctrine as 'the Akṣara-Puruṣottama Darśana' and enshrined this philosophy by consecrating mūrtis of Akṣara and Puruṣottama in exquisite, stone mandiras.[4] *Here, the text salutes him by recalling his extraordinary contributions.*

सिद्धान्तपुष्पसुफलामृतदिव्यगन्धी
यस्माद् वसन्ततिलकश्च वसन्तजन्मा।
रूढो हि यज्ञपुरुषो भुवि तत्त्ववृक्षश्
छन्दो वसन्ततिलका त्वरते सुगाने॥ ४॥

siddhāntapuṣpasuphalāmṛtadivyagandhī,
yasmād vasantatilakaśca vasantajanmā.
rūḍho hi yajñapuruṣo bhuvi tattvavṛkṣaś,
chando vasantatilakā tvarate sugāne.

<u>पदच्छेदः</u> - सिद्धान्तपुष्पसुफलामृतदिव्यगन्धी, यस्माद्, वसन्ततिलकः, च, वसन्तजन्मा, रूढः, हि यज्ञपुरुषः, भुवि, तत्त्ववृक्षः, छन्दः, वसन्ततिलका, त्वरते, सुगाने॥

<u>अन्वयः</u>

यस्माद् - because

सिद्धान्तपुष्पसुफलामृतदिव्यगन्धी - He who bristled with the ambrosial fragrance of the Akṣara-Puruṣottama philosophy, which contained the quintessence of spirituality, just as flowers and fruits contain the sweet essence of their hosts.

4 For a comprehensive analysis of Shastriji Maharaj's life and work, see Harshadrai Dave's two-volume, Gujarati work, entitled *Brahmasvarūpa Śāstrījī Mahārāj* (Swaminarayan Aksharpith, 2014).

वसन्तजन्मा - he who was born in [the beautiful season] of vasanta

वसन्ततिलकः - he who was the ornament of vasanta.

च - and

यज्ञपुरुषः - Yagnapurush

तत्त्ववृक्षः - he who was like a tree of philosophical wisdom.

भुवि - in the world

हि - indeed

रूढः - he was known

वसन्ततिलका - the vasanta-ilakā

छन्दः - metre

सुगाने - in singing his praises

त्वरते - hurries

Yagnapurushdas, as he was known throughout the world, bristled with the ambrosial fragrance of the Akṣara-Puruṣottama philosophy, which contained the quintessence of spirituality, just as flowers and fruits contain the sweet essence of their hosts. He was like a sturdy, deep-rooted tree, bounteous with philosophical wisdom. Having taken birth in vasanta, he was the ornament of this wonderful season.[5] Indeed, the vasanta-tilakā metre, personified, rushes forth to sing his glory.[6] (4)

5 'Vasanta' refers to the Indian spring season. It roughly coincides with the Gregorian months of February and March.

6 The author eulogises Shastriji Maharaj here through verses composed in vasanta-tilakā, one of the many Saṃskṛta metrical composition styles. He thus executes a play on words by making note of the Vasanta month and the vasanta-tilakā metre in succession; he then caps this inaugural stanza by personising his chosen metre, showing it to be impatient to sing the revered Shastriji Maharaj's praises.

निश्चित्य ब्रह्मपरब्रह्मस्वरूपतत्त्वं
शास्त्राच्च सद्गुरुमुखात् स्वधिया सयुक्तिम्।
प्रायोजयत् सकलबुद्धिसुचातुरीं स्वां
ब्रह्माक्षरस्य खलु डिण्डिमभव्यघोषे॥५॥

niścitya brahmaparabrahmasvarūpatattvaṃ,
śāstrācca sadgurumukhāt svadhiyā sayuktim.
prāyojayat sakalabuddhisucāturīṃ svāṃ,
brahmākṣarasya khalu ḍiṇḍimabhavyaghoṣe.

पदच्छेदः - निश्चित्य, ब्रह्मपरब्रह्मस्वरूपतत्त्वम्, शास्त्रात्, च, सद्गुरुमुखात्, स्वधिया, सयुक्तिम्, प्रायोजयत्, सकलबुद्धिसुचातुरीम्, स्वाम्, ब्रह्माक्षरस्य, खलु, डिण्डिमभव्यघोषे॥

अन्वयः

ब्रह्मपरब्रह्मस्वरूपतत्त्वम् - the forms of Akṣarabrahman and Parabrahman

निश्चित्य - with conviction

शास्त्रात् - from the śāstras

सद्गुरुमुखात् - first-hand from senior sādhus

स्वधिया च - and using his intelligence

सयुक्तिम् - using reason

(सः) - he

स्वां सकलबुद्धिचातुरीम् - all of his perception and wisdom

ब्रह्माक्षरस्य - of Akṣarabrahman

डिण्डिमभव्यघोषे - in sounding the beautiful drum

खलु - indeed

प्रायोजयत् - used

With firm conviction in Akṣarabrahman and Parabrahman, he employed the śāstras, the words of senior sādhus, reason, and his own perception and wisdom to sound the beautiful drum announcing Akṣarabrahman's greatness. (5)

कोलाहलश्च कलहश्च कुकर्मघाताः
सोढाः सुहासवदनेन प्रसादबुद्ध्या।
दुष्टा न क्वापि सरणी प्रतिकारभावात्
सिद्धान्त-सत्य-परिरक्षण-बद्ध-दृष्टेः ॥ ६ ॥

kolāhalaśca kalahaśca kukarmaghātāḥ,
soḍhāḥ suhāsavadanena prasādabuddhyā.
duṣṭā na kvāpi saraṇī pratikārabhāvāt.
siddhānta-satya-parirakṣaṇa-baddha-dṛṣṭeḥ.

पदच्छेदः - कोलाहलः, च, कलहः, च, कुकर्मघाताः, सोढाः, सुहासवदनेन, प्रसादबुद्ध्या, दुष्टा, न, क्वापि, सरणी, प्रतिकाराभावात्, सिद्धान्तसत्यपरिरक्षणबद्धदृष्टेः ॥

अन्वयः

कोलाहलः - uproar

कलहः - strife

कुकर्मघाताः च - and destructive acts

सुहासवदनेन - with a joyful countenance

प्रसादबुद्ध्या च - and with grace

(तेन) सोढाः - were tolerated by him

(अपि च) - moreover

सिद्धान्तसत्यपरिरक्षणबद्धदृष्टेः - of he who was focused on protecting truth

प्रतिकारभावात् - out of a desire for revenge

न क्वापि - not at any time

दुष्टा सरणी - the low path

(गृहीता) - taken up

He joyfully and graciously tolerated uproar, strife, and destructive acts that came his way. He never walked the low path of revenge, as he was focused on protecting truth in the form of the Akṣara-Puruṣottama philosophy. (6)

ते पञ्च साधुनियमा ननु पञ्च दिव्या
ब्रह्माक्षरं तदधिपो हरिकृष्णदेवः।
एवं समादरधृतं परमुक्तिवर्त्म
ब्रह्माण्डजीवसकलभ्रमणाव्युदासे ॥ ७ ॥

te pañca sādhuniyamā nanu pañca divyā,
brahmākṣaraṃ tadadhipo harikṛṣṇadevaḥ.
evaṃ samādaradhṛtaṃ paramuktivartma,
brahmāṇḍa-jīva-sakala-bhramaṇā-vyudāse.

पदच्छेदः - ते, पञ्च, साधुनियमाः, ननु, पञ्च, दिव्याः, ब्रह्माक्षरम्, तद्, अधिपः, हरिकृष्णदेवः, एवम्, समादरधृतम्, परमुक्तिवर्त्म, ब्रह्माण्डजीवसकलभ्रमणाव्युदासे ॥

अन्वयः

ते - with him
पञ्च (साधवः) - five sādhus
पञ्च च - and five
दिव्याः - sacred
साधुनियमाः - vows for sādhus
ननु - indeed
ब्रह्माक्षरम् - Akṣarabrahman
तदधिपः - its ruler
हरिकृष्णदेवः - Harikṛṣṇa Mahārāja (Swaminarayan)
एवम् - in this way
ब्रह्माण्डजीवसकलभ्रमणाव्युदासे - to clear the doubts of all
परमुक्तिवर्त्म - the path to ultimate liberation
समादरधृतम् - was honourably established.

He had with him just five sādhus, his five sacred vows,[7] and the entities of Akṣara and Puruṣottama. With no other possessions, he honourably established the path to ultimate liberation, which cleared the confusions of countless souls. (7)

7 Swaminarayan gave his sādhus five central vows: niṣkāma (chastity), nirlobha (abstinence from greed), nirmāna (humility), nissvāda (indifference to taste), and nissneha (non-attachment). Adherence to these vows is considered a sādhu's true ornaments and wealth.

वार्तामुपासनपरां कुरुते नितान्तं
हृद्भेदिनीं हृदयनिर्झरणामृताढ्याम्।
अर्कागमावधितया गुरुगौरवेण
ब्रह्माक्षरस्य पुरुषोत्तमसर्वकर्तुः ॥ ८ ॥

vārtāmupāsanaparāṃ kurute nitāntaṃ,
hṛdbhedinīṃ hṛdayanirjharaṇāmṛtāḍhyām.
arkāgamāvadhitayā gurugauraveṇa,
brahmākṣarasya puruṣottamasarvakartuḥ.

पदच्छेदः - वार्ताम्, उपासनपराम्, कुरुते, नितान्तम्, हृद्भेदिनीम्, हृदयनिर्झरणामृताढ्याम्, अर्कागमावधितया, गुरुगौरवेण, ब्रह्माक्षरस्य, पुरुषोत्तमसर्वकर्तुः ॥

अन्वयः

(सः) - He

नितान्तम् - incessantly

हृद्भेदिनीम् - that which pierced the heart.

हृदयनिर्झरणामृताढ्याम् - that which was like a fall of nectar flowing from his core

गुरुगौरवेण - with pride in his guru

अर्कागमावधितया - until sunrise

ब्रह्माक्षरस्य - of Akṣarabrahman

पुरुषोत्तमसर्वकर्तुः (च) - and of Puruṣottama, the omniagent

उपासनपराम् - related to upāsanā

वार्ताम् - talks

कुरुते - would do

He incessantly spoke of upāsanā. His words were like a fall of nectar flowing from his core, and his impassioned talks pierced his listeners' hearts. With pride in his guru, he would enthusiastically speak about Akṣarabrahman and Puruṣottama, the omniagent; often, his talks would continue until sunrise. (8)

श्रीवर्धमानपुर - भोगवतीतटस्थे
वृत्तालयस्थितिमता हरिधाम बद्धम्।
बोचासणे प्रमुखतीर्थकृता कृतानि
सारङ्गदुर्गनगरादिषु मन्दिराणि॥ ९॥

śrīvardhamānapura - bhogavatītaṭasthe,
vṛttālayasthitimatā haridhāma baddham.
bocāsaṇe pramukhatīrthakṛtā kṛtāni,
sāraṅga-durganagarādiṣu mandirāṇi.

पदच्छेद: - श्रीवर्धमानपुरभोगवतीतटस्थे, वृत्तालयस्थितिमता, हरिधाम, बद्धम्, बोचासणे, प्रमुखतीर्थकृता, कृतानि, सारङ्गदुर्गनरगादिषु, मन्दिराणि॥

अन्वयः

वृत्तालयस्थितिमता (तेन) - by he who resided in Vruttalaya (Vartal)

श्रीवर्धमानपुरभोगवतीतटस्थे - on the bank of the Bhogavati River in Vardhamana (Vadhvan)

हरिधाम - a mandira

बद्धम् - was built

बोचासणे - in Bochasan

सारङ्गदुर्गनगरादिषु (च) - and in Sarangpur, Durganagara (Gadhada), and other places

प्रमुखतीर्थकृता - by he who inspired significant pilgrimage sanctuaries

मन्दिराणि - mandiras

कृतानि - were built

While residing in Vruttalaya (Vartal), he built a mandira on the Bhogavati River's bank in Vardhamana (Vadhvan). The inspirer of significant pilgrimage sanctuaries, he also created mandiras in Bochasan, Sarangpur, Durganagara (Gadhada), and other locations. (9)

भिक्षाटनं प्रतिदिनं प्रभुरेकच्छत्रं
पाषाणद्रव्यसुजनातिविरक्तकालः।
न्यूनश्च साधुहरिभक्तगणस्तथापि
संस्थामहोऽयमकरोत् सुविरूढमूलाम्॥ १०॥

bhikṣāṭanaṃ pratidinaṃ prabhurekacchatraṃ,
pāṣāṇa-dravya-sujanātivirakta-kālaḥ.
nyūnaśca sādhuharibhaktagaṇastathāpi,
saṃsthāmaho'yamakarot suvirūḍhamūlām.

पदच्छेदः - भिक्षाटनम्, प्रतिदिनम्, प्रभुः, एकच्छत्रम्, पाषाणद्रव्यसुजनातिविरक्तकालः, न्यूनः, च, साधुहरिभक्तगणः, तथा, अपि, संस्थाम्, अहो, अयम्, अकरोत्, सुविरूढमूलाम्॥

अन्वयः

प्रतिदिनम् - every day

भिक्षाटनम् - roaming for alms

प्रभुः - Paramātman

एकच्छत्रम् - singular refuge

न्यूनः च - and a small

साधुहरिभक्तगणः - following of sādhus and devotees

(अवर्तन्त) - existed

अहो - Ah!

तथापि - yet still

अयम् - this person (Yagna-purushdas)

पाषाणद्रव्यसुजनातिविरक्तकालः - when stones, wealth, and workers were direly scarce

सुविरूढमूलाम् - that which has unshakeable roots

संस्थाम् - an organisation

अकरोत् - created

He begged for alms daily. Paramātman was his only shelter. Stones for construction, wealth, and workers were direly scarce. Further, he only had a small following of sādhus and devotees. Yet, he created an organisation with unshakeable roots. (10)

विश्वे ह्युपासनविधेः सुविकासहेतोर्
आनन्दब्रह्म सततं सहजो हि योगी।
वात्सल्यमूर्तिसुखदश्च प्रसन्नचेताः
स्वैक्येन दिव्यसुगुणैः परिचायितोऽस्ति॥ ११॥

viśve hyupāsanavidheḥ suvikāsahetor,
ānandabrahma satataṃ sahajo hi yogī.
vātsalyamūrtisukhadaśca prasannacetāḥ,
svaikyena divyasuguṇaiḥ paricāyito'sti.

पदच्छेदः - विश्वे, हि, उपासनविधेः, सुविकासहेतोः, आनन्दब्रह्म, सततम्, सहजः हि, योगी, वात्सल्यमूर्तिसुखदः, च, प्रसन्नचेताः, स्वैक्येन, दिव्यसुगुणैः, परिचायितः, अस्ति॥

अन्वयः

विश्वे - in the world

उपासनविधेः - of upāsanā

सुविकासहेतोः हि - for nourishment, indeed

(यज्ञपुरुषदासेन) - by Yagnapurushdas

स्वैक्येन - through his oneness

दिव्यगुणैः (च) - and through his blessed qualities

आनन्दब्रह्म - as the joyful Akṣarabrahman

सततम् - unhindered

सहजः योगी - the innate yogī

वात्सल्यमूर्तिः हि - affection personified, indeed

प्रसन्नचेताः च - he whose heart was sublime

(योगिराजः) परिचायितः अस्ति - Yogiji Maharaj was thus introduced.

To nourish this upāsanā, Yagnapurushdas introduced Yogiji Maharaj as his successor by making known his identity as Akṣarabrahman, the embodiment of joy, and by bringing to light his divine virtues – his innate perfection of yoga, personification of affection, and sublimity of mind. (11)

नैकात्मनः परममोक्षपथं विनेतुं
दीर्घेक्षणेन स्वधिया च विचक्षणोऽयम्।
उत्साह-धैर्य-करुणा-रस-सन्निपातं
योग्याशिषा मम गुरुं प्रमुखं चकार॥ १२॥

naikātmanaḥ paramamokṣapatham vinetuṃ,
dīrghekṣaṇena svadhiyā ca vicakṣaṇo'yam.
utsāha-dhairya-karuṇā-rasa-sannipātaṃ,
yogyāśiṣā mama guruṃ pramukhaṃ cakāra.

पदच्छेदः - नैकात्मनः, परममोक्षपथम्, विनेतुम्, दीर्घेक्षणेन, स्वधिया, च, विचक्षणः, अयम्, उत्साहधैर्यकरुणारससन्निपातम्, योग्याशिषा, मम, गुरुम्, प्रमुखम्, चकार॥

अन्वयः

अयम् - Yagnapurushdasji
विचक्षणः - who was wise
दीर्घेक्षणेन - through vision
स्वधिया च - and by insight
नैकात्मनः - of countless souls
परममोक्षपथम् - on the path to ultimate liberation
विनेतुम् - to take
योग्याशिषा - with Yogiji Maharaj's blessings
उत्साहधैर्यकरुणारससन्निपातम् - a blend of energy, forbearance, and compassion.
मम - my
गुरुम् - guru
प्रमुखम् - administrative head
चकार - was made

The wise Yagnapurushdas declared as 'pramukha'[8] my guru, in whom energy, forbearance, and compassion converged. This visionary and insightful decision, supported by Yogiji Maharaj's blessings, was to help take countless souls along the path to liberation. (12)

8 The author's guru, initiated as Narayanswarupdas, became known as Pramukh Swami upon being appointed as BAPS' administrative head.

1.5 Nārāyaṇasvarūpa-abhidhyāna

Pramukh Swami Maharaj, also known as Narayanaswarupdas (Nārāyaṇasvarūpadāsa), was Swaminarayan's fifth successor, the author's guru, and the inspirer of the Prasthānatrayī-svāminārāyaṇa-bhāṣyam and Svāminārāyaṇa-siddhānta-sudhā. Through the following twelve verses, the author reveres him by recalling his divine virtues.

नारायणस्वरूपोऽयं साक्षाद् ब्रह्माऽक्षरं गुरुः।
गुणाढ्यः प्रमुखः प्रेष्ठो भक्त्याऽभिध्यायते मया॥ १३॥

nārāyaṇasvarūpo'yaṃ sākṣād brahmā'kṣaraṃ guruḥ,
guṇāḍhyaḥ pramukhaḥ preṣṭho bhaktyā'bhidhyāyate mayā.

पदच्छेदः - नारायणस्वरूपः, अयम्, साक्षात्, ब्रह्म, अक्षरम्, गुरुः, गुणाढ्यः, प्रमुखः, प्रेष्ठः, भक्त्या, अभिध्यायते, मया॥

अन्वयः

अयम् - This here

नारायणस्वरूपः - Narayanswarupdas

प्रमुखः - Pramukh [Swami Maharaj]

साक्षाद् - in person

अक्षरं ब्रह्म - Akṣarabrahman

गुणाढ्यः - one who has abundant virtues

प्रेष्ठः - one who is dearly beloved

गुरुः - guru

मया - by me

भक्त्या - with devotion

अभिध्यायते - is contemplated upon

This here Narayanswarupdas, or Pramukh Swami Maharaj, is the Akṣarabrahman guru in person. He possesses abundant virtues and is dearly beloved. I devoutly contemplate upon him. (13)

ब्रह्मासि सच्चिदानन्दो निर्विकल्पसमाधिमान्।
निरंशो निर्विकारोऽसि देहावस्थापरस्तथा॥ १४॥

brahmāsi saccidānando nirvikalpasamādhimān,
niraṃśo nirvikāro'si dehāvasthāparastathā.

<u>पदच्छेदः</u> - ब्रह्म, असि, सच्चिदानन्दः, निर्विकल्पसमाधिमान्, निरंशः, निर्विकारः, असि, देहावस्थापरः, तथा॥

<u>अन्वयः</u>

(त्वम्) - You

ब्रह्म - Akṣarabrahman

सच्चिदानन्दः - truth, sentience, and bliss

निर्विकल्पसमाधिमान् - one who has attained nirvikalpa samadhi.

असि - are

तथा - also

(त्वम्) - you

निरंशः - undivided

निर्विकारः - flawless

देहावस्थापरः - above the body's states of being

असि - are

You are Akṣarabrahman. You are the very embodiment of truth, sentience, and bliss. You have attained nirvikalpa samādhi. Moreover, you are undivided, flawless, and above the body's states of being. (14)

अनादिकालतः सर्वमायिकोपाधिवर्जितः ।
पञ्चसु वर्तमानेषु नित्यमखण्डितस्थितिः ॥ १५ ॥

anādikālataḥ sarvamāyikopādhivarjitaḥ,
pañcasu vartamāneṣu nityamakhaṇḍitasthitiḥ.

पदच्छेदः - अनादिकालतः, सर्वमायिकोपाधिवर्जितः, पञ्चसु, वर्तमानेषु, नित्यम्, अखण्डितस्थितिः ॥

अन्वयः

(त्वम्) - you

अनादिकालतः - eternally

सर्वमायिकोपाधिवर्जितः - free from all bonds caused by māyā

पञ्चसु वर्तमानेषु - in the five vows

नित्यम् - always

अखण्डितस्थितिः - entirely established

(असि) - you are

You are eternally free from māyā's shackles and are ever immersed in adhering to the five principle vows of a sādhu.[9] (15)

9 See footnote 7.

स्थितप्रज्ञः परो योगी निवृत्तोऽसि प्रवर्तने।
ज्ञानवाँश्च गुणातीतः प्रेष्ठोऽसि सर्वतो हरेः ॥ १६ ॥

sthitaprajñaḥ paro yogī nivṛtto'si pravartane,
jñānavāṁścha guṇātītaḥ preṣṭho'si sarvato hareḥ.

पदच्छेदः - स्थितप्रज्ञः, परः, योगी, निवृत्तः, असि, प्रवर्तने, ज्ञानवान्, च, गुणातीतः, प्रेष्ठः, असि, सर्वतः, हरेः ॥

अन्वयः

(त्वम्) - You

स्थितप्रज्ञः - sthitaprajña[12]

परः - preeminent

योगी - yogī

प्रवर्तने - while being engaged

निवृत्तः - one who is detached

असि - are

ज्ञानवान् - wise

गुणातीतः - guṇātīta (one who is above māyā's qualities)

सर्वतः - in every way

च - and

हरेः - Paramātman's

प्रेष्ठः - dearest

असि - are

You are the sthitaprajña,[10] preeminent yogī. You are engaged in service, yet you are eternally detached. You are wise, guṇātīta (above māyā's qualities), and Paramātman's dearest in every way. (16)

10 'Sthitaprajña' is one of the most well-known terms the *Bhagavadgītā* uses to describe the quintessential devotee (verses 2.54-72). By using this term to describe Pramukh Swami Maharaj, the author indicates that his guru is the living example of the *Gītā*'s core teachings.

परमैकान्तिको भक्तो दिव्यभावरतः सदा।
निश्चयस्ते निरुत्थान उत्तमनिर्विकल्पकः ॥ १७ ॥

paramaikāntiko bhakto divyabhāvarataḥ sadā,
niścayaste nirutthāna uttamanirvikalpakaḥ.

पदच्छेदः - परमैकान्तिकः, भक्तः, दिव्यभावरतः, सदा, निश्चयः, ते, निरुत्थानः, उत्तमनिर्विकल्पकः ॥

अन्वयः

(त्वम्) - you

परमैकान्तिकः - the parama ekāntika

भक्तः - bhakta

सदा - always

दिव्यभावरतः - engrossed in divyabhāva (the thought that all are divine)

(असि) - are

ते - your

निश्चयः - faith

निरूत्थानः - that which is unmoveable

उत्तमनिर्विकल्पकः - the highest form of that which is unwavering

(च अस्ति) - and is

You are the parama ekāntika bhakta.[11] You are engrossed in divyabhāva (the thought that all are divine). Your faith is unmoveable and is characterised by the highest form of unwavering conviction.[12] (17)

11 The Akṣarabrahman guru is known, interchangeably, through such monikers as the param ekāntika bhakta, sādhu, satpuruṣa, ekāntika, guru, and mahāpuruṣa; at once embodying both Akṣarabrahman and Parabrahman, the guru is also known as brahmasvarūpa and guru-hari (see verses 163-64, 141).

12 Developing such conviction, known as uttama nirvikalpa niścaya, is the singular goal of all spiritual praxis (Vacanāmṛta L-12; Swaminarayan 290-92).

ज्ञानयज्ञमयो नित्यं श्रीहर्याज्ञानुपालकः ।
व्यतियन्ति दिवारात्रं भगवत्कीर्तनादिषु ॥ १८ ॥

jñānayajñamayo nityaṃ śrīharyājñānupālakaḥ,
vyatiyanti divārātraṃ bhagavatkīrtanādiṣu.

पदच्छेदः - ज्ञानयज्ञमयः, नित्यम्, श्रीहरिः, आज्ञानुपालकः, व्यतियन्ति, दिवारात्रम्, भगवत्कीर्ततनादिषु ॥

अन्वयः

(त्वम्) - you

नित्यम् - continually

ज्ञानयज्ञमयः - engrossed in the jñānayajña

श्रीहर्याज्ञानुपालकः - one who follows Shri Hari's (Bhagwan Swaminarayan's) ordinances

(असि) - are

(भवतः) - your

दिवारात्रम् - days and nights

भगवत्कीर्तनादिषु - in God's kīrtana bhakti and other such activities

व्यतियन्ति - pass

You are continually engrossed in the jñānayajña.[13] You follow Shri Hari's (Bhagwan Swaminarayan's) ordinances and spend your days and nights engaged in kīrtana-bhakti and other such devotional activities. (18)

---

13 The *Bhagavadgītā*'s fourth canto discusses many different types of yajñas, foremost of which is the jñānayajña. Swaminarayan defines the jñānayajña as the cognitive practise of identifying oneself with Akṣarabrahman and offering upāsanā to Parabrahman (Vacanāmṛta GM-8; Swaminarayan 364–68).

श्रीहरिपरभावज्ञः सेव्योऽपि भगवानिव।
वर्तसे त्वं सदादासः स्वामिसेवकभावतः ॥ १९ ॥

śrīhariparabhāvajñaḥ sevyo'pi bhagavāniva,
vartase tvaṃ sadādāsaḥ svāmisevakabhāvataḥ.

पदच्छेदः - श्रीहरिपरभावज्ञः, सेव्यः, अपि, भगवान्, इव, वर्तसे, त्वम्, सदादासः, स्वामिसेवकभावतः ॥

अन्वयः

(त्वम्) - you

श्रीहरिपरभावज्ञः - the knower of Shri Hari's (Swaminarayan's) supreme greatness

भगवान् - Paramātman

इव - like

सेव्यः - worthy of being served

अपि - also

स्वामिसेवकभावतः - with a disposition like that of a servant before his master

सदादासः - always a servant

वर्तसे - behave

You are the knower of Shri Hari's (Swaminarayan's) supreme greatness, and you are worthy of being served as Paramātman himself. Your manner is like that of a servant before his master; thus, you always behave like a humble servant. (19)

परमात्मस्वरूपस्य त्वं हि निश्चायको गुरुः।
अनादिकर्मजा माया त्वयैव तु विदार्यते॥ २०॥

paramātmasvarūpasya tvaṃ hi niścāyako guruḥ,
anādikarmajā māyā tvayaiva tu vidāryate.

पदच्छेदः - परमात्मस्वरूपस्य, त्वम्, हि, निश्चायकः, गुरुः, अनादिकर्मजा, माया, त्वया, एव, तु, विदार्यते॥

अन्वयः

त्वम् - you

हि - indeed

परमात्मस्वरूपस्य - of Paramātman's form

निश्चायकः - one who establishes conviction

गुरुः - the guru

(असि) - are

त्वया - by you

एव - alone

अनादिकर्मजा - born of timeless karma

माया - māyā

तु - certainly

विदार्यते - is revoked

You indeed are the guru that establishes conviction in Paramātman's form. Certainly, you alone can revoke māyā, which is born of timeless karma. (20)

यथावत् प्रभुमाहात्म्यं धर्म एकान्तिकस्तथा ।
ब्रह्मभावः स्वसङ्गेन प्रस्थाप्यते मदात्मनि ॥ २१ ॥

yathāvat prabhumāhātmyaṃ dharma ekāntikastathā,
brahmabhāvaḥ svasaṅgena prasthāpyate madātmani.

पदच्छेदः - यथावत्, प्रभुमाहात्म्यम्, धर्मः, एकान्तिकः, तथा, ब्रह्मभावः, स्वसङ्गेन, प्रस्थाप्यते, मदात्मनि ॥

अन्वयः

स्वसङ्गेन - through your association

मदात्मनि - in my heart

प्रभुमाहात्म्यम् - Paramātman's greatness

यथावत् - as it is

एकान्तिकः धर्मः - ekāntika dharma

तथा - and

ब्रह्मभावः - brahmabhāva

प्रस्थाप्यते - are established

Your company thoroughly establishes Paramātman's greatness, ekāntika dharma,[14] and brahmabhāva[15] within my heart. (21)

---

14 Ekāntika dharma is the pinnacle of spiritual achievement; it is characterised by the perfection of dharma, jñāna, vairāgya, and bhakti (see verses 148-60).

15 Brahmabhāva is another way of describing spiritual perfection; it signifies the ātman's qualitative oneness with Akṣarabrahman. Other words for brahmabhāva are brahmasthiti and brāhmī sthiti. One who has attained this state is known as being brahmarūpa (see verses 145-47).

दिव्योऽसि मद्गुरुः साक्षात् त्वं परब्रह्मधारकः ।
मोक्षो ब्राह्मी स्थितिश्चैव कराग्रे ते प्रसङ्गतः ॥ २२ ॥

divyo'si madguruḥ sākṣāt tvaṃ parabrahmadhārakaḥ,
mokṣo brāhmī sthitiścaiva karāgre te prasaṅgataḥ.

पदच्छेदः - दिव्यः, असि, मद्गुरुः, साक्षात्, त्वम्, परब्रह्मधारकः, मोक्षः, ब्राह्मी, स्थितिः, च, एव, कराग्रे, ते, प्रसङ्गतः ॥

अन्वयः

(त्वम्) - you

साक्षात् - directly

परब्रह्मधारकः - one who beholds Parabrahman

दिव्यः - divine

मद्गुरुः - my guru

असि - are

ते प्रसङ्गतः - through your communion

मोक्षः - liberation

ब्राह्मी स्थितिः - the state of being brahmarūpa

च - and

कराग्रे - in the palm of the hand

एव - just

(अस्ति) - is

You directly behold Parabrahman within you. You are divine, and you are my guru. Through your communion, liberation and the state of being brahmarūpa rest in the palm of my hand. (22)

एवं ध्यात्वा त्वदाज्ञायामनुवृत्तौ च वर्तनम्।
सर्वथा सर्वदा भूयात् प्रार्थये भद्रभावतः॥ २३ ॥

evaṃ dhyātvā tvadājñāyāmanuvṛttau ca vartanam,
sarvathā sarvadā bhūyāt prārthaye bhadrabhāvataḥ.

पदच्छेदः - एवम्, ध्यात्वा, त्वदाज्ञायाम्, अनुवृत्तौ, च, वर्तनम्, सर्वथा, सर्वदा, भूयात्, प्रार्थये, भद्रभावतः ॥

अन्वयः

(अहम्) - I

एवम् - in this way

ध्यात्वा - having meditated

त्वदाज्ञायाम् अनुवृत्तौ च - within your ordinances and wishes

सर्वथा - in every way

सर्वदा च - and always

(मम) - my

वर्तनम् - behaviour

भूयाद् - may be

(इति) - the aforementioned

भद्रभावतः - auspiciously

प्रार्थये - pray

Having meditated upon you in this way, I auspiciously pray that I may always act according to your divine ordinances and wishes in every way. (23)

शुद्धभावेन यो भक्तो ब्रह्ममन्ता भवेद् हृदा।
साक्षात्कुर्यात् परं ब्रह्म ब्रह्मरूपे निजात्मनि॥ २४॥

śuddhabhāvena yo bhakto brahmamantā bhaved hṛdā,
sākṣātkuryāt paraṃ brahma brahmarūpe nijātmani.

पदच्छेदः - शुद्धभावेन, यः, भक्तः, ब्रह्ममन्ता, भवेत्, हृदा, साक्षात्कुर्यात्, परम्, ब्रह्म, ब्रह्मरूपे, निजात्मनि॥

अन्वयः

यः भक्तः - the devotee who

शुद्धभावेन - with sincerity

हृदा - from the heart

ब्रह्ममन्ता - one who meditates on Akṣarabrahman

भवेत् - becomes

(सः) - such a devotee

ब्रह्मरूपे निजात्मनि - in their brahmarūpa ātman

परं ब्रह्म - Parabrahman

साक्षात्कुर्यात् - realises

A devotee who meditates on the Akṣarabrahman guru with heartfelt sincerity will realise Parabrahman in their brahmarūpa ātman. (24)

1.6 Abhyarthanā

Lastly, the author offers his prayers to Mahant Swami Maharaj, who is Swaminarayan's sixth successor and the manifest, Akṣarabrahman guru.

गुरुरेव मम ध्यानं व्याख्यानं मे गुरुः सदा।
गुरुरेव मम ज्ञानं सुगानं गुरुरेव च॥ २५॥

gurureva mama dhyānaṃ vyākhyānaṃ me guruḥ sadā,
gurureva mama jñānaṃ sugānaṃ gurureva ca.

पदच्छेदः - गुरुः, एव, मम, ध्यानम्, व्याख्यानम्, मे, गुरुः, सदा, गुरुः, एव, मम, ज्ञानम्, सुगानम्, गुरुः, एव, च॥

अन्वयः

सदा - at all times
गुरुः - the guru
एव - alone
मम - my
ध्यानम् - the object of meditation
गुरुः - the guru
(एव) - alone
मे - my
व्याख्यानम् - the object of speech
गुरुः - the guru
एव - alone
मम - my
ज्ञानम् - the object of wisdom
गुरुः - the guru
च - and
एव - alone
(मे) - my
सुगानम् - the object of poetic verses
(अस्ति) - is

The guru alone is forever the core of my meditations. The guru alone is the subject of my speech. The guru alone is the centre of my knowledge. The guru alone is the locus of my poetic verses. (25)

महन्तस्वामिनं नौमि ब्रह्मविद्याप्रबोधकम्।
निर्वैरं परमं शान्तं कृपालुं मे गुरुं प्रियम्॥ २६॥

mahantasvāminaṃ naumi brahmavidyāprabodhakam,
nirvairaṃ paramaṃ śāntaṃ kṛpāluṃ me guruṃ priyam.

<u>पदच्छेद:</u> - महन्तस्वामिनम्, नौमि, ब्रह्मविद्याप्रबोधकम्, निर्वैरम्, परमम्, शान्तम्, कृपालुम्, मे, गुरुम्, प्रियम्॥

<u>अन्वय:</u>

निर्वैरम् - one who is absent of enmity

परमम् - utmost

शान्तम् - one who is peaceful

कृपालुम् - compassionate

ब्रह्मविद्याप्रबोधकम् - one who gives people the knowledge of brahmavidyā.

मे - my

प्रियम् - dear

गुरुम् - guru

महन्तस्वामिनम् - to Mahant Swami

(अहम्) - I

नौमि - bow

I bow to my dear guru Mahant Swami Maharaj, the torchbearer of brahmavidyā; he harbours enmity towards none, experiences utmost peace, and is compassionate. (26)

1.7 The Swaminarayan Mantra's Significance

श्रीहरिः सहजानन्दः स्वयमुपदिदेश यम्।
स्वामिनारायणं मन्त्रं गर्भितं ब्रह्मविद्यया॥ २७॥

śrīhariḥ sahajānandaḥ svayamupadideśa yam,
svāminārāyaṇaṃ mantraṃ garbhitaṃ brahmavidyayā.

<u>पदच्छेदः</u> - श्रीहरिः, सहजानन्दः, स्वयम्, उपदिदेश, यम्, स्वामिनारायणम्, मन्त्रम्, गर्भितम्, ब्रह्मविद्यया॥

<u>अन्वयः</u>

श्रीहरिः - Shri Hari

सहजानन्दः - Sahajanand (Bhagwan Swaminarayan)

स्वयम् - himself

यम् - that

स्वामिनारायणम् - Swaminarayan

मन्त्रम् - mantra

उपदिदेश - taught

(तम्) - this

ब्रह्मविद्यया - with brahmavidyā[18]

गर्भितम् - embedded with

(अस्ति) - is

The Swaminarayan mantra was given by Shri Hari Sahajanand (Bhagwan Swaminarayan) himself. The concept of brahmavidyā[16] is embedded in this mantra. (27)

---

16 Muṇḍakopaniṣad 1.2.13 defines brahmavidyā as the knowledge of Akṣara and Puruṣottama (Bhadreshdas, *Upaniṣat-svāminārāyaṇa-bhāṣyam*, Vol.1, 256-57). This very knowledge of brahmavidyā is also encapsulated within the Swaminarayan mantra, as described in verse 28 of the present text.

अक्षरं ब्रह्म विज्ञेयं मन्त्रे स्वामीति शब्दतः ।
नारायणेति शब्देन तत्परः पुरुषोत्तमः ॥ २८ ॥

akṣaraṃ brahma vijñeyaṃ mantre svāmīti śabdataḥ,
nārāyaṇeti śabdena tatparaḥ puruṣottamaḥ.

पदच्छेदः - अक्षरम्, ब्रह्म, विज्ञेयम्, मन्त्रे, स्वामी, इति, शब्दतः, नारायण, इति, शब्देन, तत्परः, पुरुषोत्तमः ॥

अन्वयः

(तस्मिन्) मन्त्रे - in this mantra

स्वामी इति - 'Svāmī'

शब्दतः - from [this] word

अक्षरं ब्रह्म - Akṣarabrahman

विज्ञेयम् - should be understood

नारायण इति - 'Nārāyaṇa'

शब्देन - from [this] word

तत्परः - that which is above Akṣarabrahman

पुरुषोत्तमः - Puruṣottama

(विज्ञेयः) - should be understood.

In this mantra, the word 'Svāmī' should be understood to signify Akṣarabrahman and the word 'Nārāyaṇa' should be understood to denote Puruṣottama, who is above Akṣarabrahman. (28)

1.8 The Five Eternal Entities

जीवस्तथेश्वरो माया ब्रह्म परमब्रह्म च।
नित्याः सत्याः सदैवैते मिथो भिन्नाः स्वरूपतः ॥ २९ ॥

jīvastatheśvaro māyā brahma paramabrahma ca,
nityāḥ satyāḥ sadaivaite mitho bhinnāḥ svarūpataḥ.

पदच्छेदः - जीवः, तथा, ईश्वरः, माया, ब्रह्म, परमब्रह्म, च, नित्याः, सत्याः, सदा, एव, एते, मिथः, भिन्नाः, स्वरूपतः ।

अन्वयः

जीवः - the jīva

ईश्वरः - the īśvara

माया - māyā

ब्रह्म - Akṣarabrahman

तथा - and

परब्रह्म - Parabrahman

एते - these

(पदार्थाः) - entities

सदा - eternally

एव - indeed

नित्याः - eternal

सत्याः - true

स्वरूपतः - inherently

मिथः च - and from one another

भिन्नाः - distinct

The entities of the jīva, īśvara, māyā, Akṣarabrahman, and Parabrahman are eternal, true, and ontologically distinct from one another. (29)

स्वामिनारायणेनैवं पदार्थाः पञ्च कीर्तिताः।
यज्ज्ञानात् कृत्स्नतां याति ब्रह्मविद्याऽपवर्गदा॥ ३०॥

svāminārāyaṇenaivaṃ padārthāḥ pañca kīrtitāḥ,
yajjñānāt kṛtsnatāṃ yāti brahmavidyā'pavargadā.

पदच्छेदः - स्वामिनारायणेन, एवम्, पदार्थाः, पञ्च, कीर्तिताः, यज्ज्ञानात्, कृत्स्नताम्, याति, ब्रह्मविद्या, अपवर्गदा॥

अन्वयः

स्वामिनारायणेन - by Swaminarayan

एवम् - in this way

पञ्च पदार्थाः - five entities

कीर्तिताः - proclaimed

यज्ज्ञानाद् - by whose knowledge

अपवर्गदा - that which gives liberation

ब्रह्मविद्या - brahmavidyā

कृत्स्नताम् - fulfilment

याति - attains

Bhagwan Swaminarayan proclaimed five entities in this way; understanding these entities leads to the fulfilment of brahmavidyā, which grants liberation. (30)

In 2008, Brahmaswarup Pramukh Swami Maharaj wrote a letter encompassing Bhagwan Swaminarayan's Akṣara-Puruṣottama Darśana. Here, the author describes this letter as the basis for the Svāminārāyaṇa-siddhānta-sudhā.

सत्यसिद्धान्तसर्वस्वं सहजानन्दबोधितम्।
अभ्यलिखत् स्वयं पत्रे स्वाऽक्षरैः प्रमुखो गुरुः ॥ ३१ ॥

satyasiddhāntasarvasvaṃ sahajānandabodhitam,
abhyalikhatsvayaṃpatresvā'kṣaraiḥpramukhoguruḥ.

पदच्छेदः - सत्यसिद्धान्तसर्वस्वम्, सहजानन्दबोधितम्, अभ्यलिखत्, स्वयम्, पत्रे, स्वाऽक्षरैः, प्रमुखः, गुरुः ॥

अन्वयः

गुरुः - Guru

प्रमुखः - Pramukh Swami Maharaj

स्वाऽक्षरैः - in his own handwriting

सहजानन्दबोधितम् - taught by Sahajanand

सत्यसिद्धान्तसर्वस्वम् - the bounty in the form of this truthful principle

स्वयम् - himself

पत्रे - in a letter

अभ्यलिखत् - wrote

Sahajanand Swami (Bhagwan Swaminarayan) revealed an extraordinary bounty in the form of this truthful principle, which Guru Pramukh Swami Maharaj penned in a letter written in his own handwriting. (31)

पत्रव्याख्यानरूपोऽयं सुधाग्रन्थो हि केवलम्।
तदुपदेशवाक्यानां स्यान्मननमहोत्सवः ॥ ३२ ॥

patravyākhyānarūpo'yaṃ sudhāgrantho hi kevalam
tadupadeśavākyānāṃ syānmananamahotsavaḥ.

पदच्छेदः - पत्रव्याख्यानरूपः, अयम्, सुधाग्रन्थः, हि, केवलम्, तदुपदेशवाक्यानाम्, स्यात्, मननमहोत्सवः ॥

अन्वयः

अयम् - this

सुधाग्रन्थः - text known as the *Sudhā*

केवलम् - merely

पत्रव्याख्यानरूपः - in the form of an explanation of this letter

हि - indeed

तदुपदेशवाक्यानाम् - of its teachings

मननमहोत्सवः - a reflective celebration

स्यात् - is

This text, known as the *Sudhā*,[17] is merely an explanation of this letter. Indeed, it is but a reflective celebration of its teachings. (32)

---

17 The *Svāminārāyaṇa-siddhānta-sudhā*.

एवं परब्रह्मस्वामिनारायणप्रबोधित-ब्रह्मस्वरूपगुणातीतगुरुपरम्परोपबृंहित-
ब्रह्मविद्यालक्षणाऽक्षरपुरुषोत्तमदर्शनप्रतिपादके
साधुभद्रेशदासविरचिते
स्वामिनारायणसिद्धान्तसुधाऽऽख्ये शास्त्रेऽस्मिन्
समाप्तं मङ्गलधारा नाम
प्रथमं प्रकरणम् ॥

In this way ends the first chapter, known as the 'Maṅgala-dhārā', of Sadhu Bhadreshdas' *Svāminārāyaṇa-siddhānta-sudhā*, a text that substantiates the Akṣara-Puruṣottama Darśana, which is characterised as brahmavidyā, was taught by Parabrahman Swaminarayan, and has been fostered by the lineage of brahmasvarūpa, guṇātīta gurus.

Chapter 2

Akṣarabrahma-dhārā

2.1 Introduction

One of the most distinctive features of the Akṣara-Puruṣottama Darśana is its acceptance of a divine entity known as Akṣarabrahman that is ontologically distinct from the omnipotent Puruṣottama. Recognising, understanding, and associating with this entity, according to the Akṣara-Puruṣottama Darśana, is key to realising Puruṣottama's greatness and attaining liberation.

Bhadreshdas Swami thus begins his discussion of the Akṣara-Puruṣottama Darśana by explaining Akṣarabrahman's nature, form, and significance. Thereafter, he celebrates Akṣarabrahman's presence on earth today in the form of the brahmasvarūpa guru.

The knowledge of Akṣarabrahman was, indeed, ensconced in the Vedas and Upaniṣads, Bhadreshdas writes. However, it was Parabrahman Swaminarayan and his successor Gunatitanand Swami (Guṇātītānanda Svāmī), the manifest form of Akṣarabrahman, who first brought this knowledge to light through their teachings.

Bhadreshdas next offers an etymological analysis of the word 'Akṣarabrahman', explaining that 'Akṣara' signifies the entity's ubiquity and immutability, whereas 'Brahman' signifies its extraordinary pervasiveness. He explains that Akṣarabrahman is rightfully named as such, given that it is immutable and more pervasive than the jīva, īśvara, and māyā. Indeed, only Paramātmān transcends this entity. Paramātmān is thus known as Parabrahman (literally, that which is superior to Akṣarabrahman).

Thereafter, the author describes Akṣarabrahman's four forms: (1) the cidākāśa, (2) the divine abode, (3) the servant in the divine abode, and (4) the manifest guru.

The first of these four forms, the cidākāśa, pervades and sustains all of creation. The second form, the abode, is where liberated beings go to eternally enjoy Paramātmān's bliss in the afterlife. The third of the forms listed above is that which serves Paramātmān in Akṣaradhāman. The fourth is that which comes to earth as the guru. This Akṣarabrahman guru is a vessel through which Paramātmān engages with people on earth, acts as an ideal for spiritual seekers, and grants liberation.

Upon denoting Akṣarabrahman's four forms, the author clarifies that the distinctions presented here are merely due to Akṣarabrahman's various service roles; intrinsically Akṣarabrahman is but one existential entity.

The author concludes by stating Akṣarabrahman's prevalence in the śāstras. Specifically, he says that there is not a single Upaniṣad nor a single chapter from the *Brahmasūtras*, the *Bhagavadgītā*, or the Vacanāmṛta that does not mention Akṣarabrahman's glory.

In this way, Bhadreshdas begins his discussion of the Akṣara-Puruṣottama Darśana by explicating Akṣarabrahman, the most definitive and distinctive element informing the darśana's orthodoxy.

2.2 Benediction

The Akṣarabrahma-dhārā begins with entreaties that venerate Akṣarabrahman and pronounce this entity's significant role in spiritual praxis:

गुणातीतं गुरुं प्राप्य ब्रह्म रूपं निजात्मनः ।
विभाव्य दासभावेन स्वामिनारायणं भजे ॥ ३३ ॥

gunātītaṃ guruṃ prāpya brahma rūpaṃ nijātmanaḥ,
vibhāvya dāsabhāvena svāminārāyaṇaṃ bhaje.

<u>पदच्छेदः</u> - गुणातीतम्, गुरुम्, प्राप्य, ब्रह्म, रूपम्, निजात्मनः, विभाव्य, दासभावेन, स्वामिनारायणम्, भजे ॥

<u>अन्वयः</u>

(अहं) - I
गुणातीतम् - the guṇātīta
गुरुम् - guru
प्राप्य - having attained
निजात्मानः - my ātman
ब्रह्म रूपम् - brahmarūpa
विभाव्य - believing
दासभावेन - with humility
स्वामिनारायणम् - Swaminarayan
भजे - worship

I humbly worship Bhagwan Swaminarayan, having attained the guṇātīta guru and believing my ātman to be brahmarūpa. (33)

ब्राह्मी स्थितिर्यतः सिद्ध्येत् प्राकट्यं परब्रह्मणः ।
ब्रह्माऽक्षरं गुरुं वन्दे साक्षात् सिद्धान्तरूपिणम् ॥ ३४ ॥

brāhmī sthitiryataḥ siddhyet prākaṭyaṃ parabrahmaṇaḥ,
brahmā'kṣaraṃ guruṃ vande sākṣāt siddhāntarūpiṇam.

पदच्छेदः - ब्राह्मी, स्थितिः, यतः, सिद्ध्येत्, प्राकट्यम्, परब्रह्मणः, ब्रह्म, अक्षरम्, गुरुम्, वन्दे, साक्षात्, सिद्धान्तरूपिणम् ॥

अन्वयः

यतः - through whom

ब्राह्मी - related to Akṣarabrahman

स्थितिः - state

सिद्ध्येत् - can be achieved

परब्रह्मणः (च) - and Parabrahman's

(यतः) - through whom

प्राकट्यम् - manifestation

(भवेत्) - occurs

(तादृशम्) - such

साक्षात् - the very

सिद्धान्तरूपिणम् - embodier of the [Akṣara-Puruṣottama] philosophy

ब्रह्माक्षरम् - to the Akṣarabrahman

गुरुम् - guru

(अहम्) - I

वन्दे - bow

I bow to the Akṣarabrahman guru, through whom one can attain the Brāhmic state, through whom Parabrahman manifests, and who is the very embodiment of the Akṣara-Puruṣottama philosophy. (34)

2.3 Novelty

The following two verses describe Bhagwan Swaminarayan and his first successor, Akṣarabrahman Gunatitanand Swami, enriching Indian philosophy by elucidating the entity of Akṣarabrahman.

वेदवेदान्तशास्त्रेषु प्रच्छन्नं गूढमक्षरम्।
प्रथममुज्जुघोषाऽत्र स्वामिनारायणो भुवि॥ ३५॥

vedavedāntaśāstreṣu pracchannaṃ gūḍhamakṣaram,
prathamamujjughoṣā'tra svāminārāyaṇo bhuvi.

पदच्छेदः - वेदवेदान्तशास्त्रेषु, प्रच्छन्नम्, गूढम्, अक्षरम्, प्रथमम्, उज्जुघोष, अत्र, स्वामिनारायणः, भुवि॥

अन्वयः

वेदवेदान्तशास्त्रेषु - in the Vedas and Upaniṣads

गूढम् - esoteric

अक्षरम् - Akṣarabrahman

(तत्त्वम्) - the entity

प्रच्छन्नम् - concealed

(आसीत्) - was

(तत्) - it

स्वामिनारायणः - Swaminarayan

अत्र - here

भुवि - in the world

प्रथमम् - first

उज्जुघोष - declared

The esoteric entity of Akṣarabrahman was concealed within the Vedas and Upaniṣads. It was first revealed to the world by Bhagwan Swaminarayan. (35)

स्वीयोपदेशवार्तासु गुणातीतेन ब्रह्मणा।
स्वरूपं स्वयमेवोक्तं तस्माद् ब्रह्म प्रमाणितम्॥ ३६॥

svīyopadeśavārtāsu guṇātītena brahmaṇāsvarūpaṃ,
svayamevoktaṃ tasmād brahma pramāṇitam.

पदच्छेदः - स्वीयोपदेशवार्तासु, गुणातीतेन, ब्रह्मणा, स्वरूपम्, स्वयम्, एव, उक्तम्, तस्मात्, ब्रह्म, प्रमाणितम्॥

अन्वयः

गुणातीतेन - by Gunatitanand Swami

ब्रह्मणा - [who was] the form of Akṣarabrahman

स्वीयोपदेशवार्तासु - in his own teachings

स्वरूपम् - the form [of Akṣarabrahman]

स्वयम् - himself

एव - indeed

उक्तम् - was explained

तस्मात् - therefore

ब्रह्म - Akṣarabrahman

प्रमाणितम् - was verified

Moreover, Akṣarabrahman Gunatitanand Swami himself explained, and thereby verified, Akṣarabrahman's form within his own discourses.[18] (36)

---

18 Gunatitanand Swami's discourses were compiled in the form of a text known as the Svāmīnī Vāto.

2.4 Akṣarabrahman's Soteriological Significance

The author then explains Akṣarabrahman's foundational significance for those trotting on the spiritual path.

परोपासनसिद्ध्यर्थं ब्रह्मभावाऽऽप्तये तथा।
निर्विघ्नभक्तिसम्पत्त्यै ब्रह्मज्ञानमपेक्षितम्॥ ३७॥

paropāsanasiddhyartham̤ brahmabhāvā''ptaye tathā,
nirvighnabhaktisampattyai brahmajñānamapekṣitam.

<u>पदच्छेदः</u> - परोपासनसिद्ध्यर्थम्, ब्रह्मभावाऽऽप्तये, तथा, निर्विघ्नभक्तिसम्पत्त्यै, ब्रह्मज्ञानम्, अपेक्षितम्॥

<u>अन्वयः</u>

परोपासनसिद्ध्यर्थम् - to attain Parabrahman's upāsanā.

ब्रह्मभावाऽऽप्तये - to attain brahmabhāva

तथा - and

निर्विघ्नभक्तिसम्पत्त्यै - to attain unhindered bhakti

ब्रह्मज्ञानमपेक्षितम् - knowledge of Akṣarabrahman is required

Knowledge of Akṣarabrahman is required to attain Parabrahman's upāsanā, brahmabhāva, and unhindered bhakti.[19] (37)

19 Bhadreshdas explains in the *Svāminārāyaṇa-siddhānta-sudhā* (p.307-15) that the verse 'brahma veda brahmaiva bhavati' (Muṇḍakopaniṣad 3.2.9) posits that one who knows Akṣarabrahman becomes like Akṣarabrahman. The verse explicated above, while enumerating the necessity of attaining oneness with Akṣarabrahman, also puts forth some of the most significant qualities of one who attains this state.

2.5 An Etymological Analysis

Having established Akṣarabrahman's importance, the author elucidates the two words that make up the entity's name, 'Akṣara' and 'Brahman', based on Saṃskṛta grammar and linguistics.

अश्नोतेर्व्यापनार्थाद्धि नञ्पूर्वात्क्षरतेस्तथा।
व्युत्पन्नोऽक्षरशब्दोऽयं ब्रह्मण्येव प्रयुज्यते॥ ३८॥

aśnotervyāpanārthāddhi nañpūrvātkṣaratestathā,
vyutpanno'kṣaraśabdo'yaṃ brahmaṇyeva prayujyate.

पदच्छेदः - अश्नोतेः, व्यापनार्थात्, हि, नञ्पूर्वात्, क्षरतेः, तथा, व्युत्पन्नः, अक्षरशब्दः, अयम्, ब्रह्मणि, एव, प्रयुज्यते॥

अन्वयः

अश्नोतेः व्यापनार्थात् - from the meaning of the verb aśnoti reflecting pervasiveness

हि - certainly

तथा - and

नञ्पूर्वात् क्षरतेः - from the verb kṣarati, preceded by the prefix 'nañ'

व्युत्पन्नः - to be derived

अयम् अक्षरशब्दः - this word, 'Akṣara'

ब्रह्मणि - in the sense of Akṣarabrahman

एव - indeed

प्रयुज्यते - is used

The word 'Akṣara' is derived either from the verb 'aśnoti', which means to pervade, or 'kṣarati', preceded by the prefix 'nañ' (together meaning that which does not decay). Accordingly, the word 'Akṣara' is used to describe Akṣarabrahman. (38)

सर्वजीवेश्वरेभ्यश्च मायातन्मुक्ततस्तथा।
बृहत्त्वाद् बृंहणत्वाच्च ब्रह्मेत्यक्षरमुच्यते॥ ३९॥

sarvajīveśvarebhyaśca māyātanmuktatastathā,
bṛhattvād bṛṃhaṇatvācca brahmetyakṣaramucyate.

पदच्छेदः - सर्वजीवेश्वरेभ्यः, च, मायातन्मुक्ततः, तथा, बृहत्त्वात्, बृंहणत्त्वात्, च, ब्रह्म, इति, अक्षरम्, उच्यते॥

अन्वयः

सर्वजीवेश्वरेभ्यः - than all of the jīvas and īśvaras

तथा च - and also

मायातन्मुक्ततः - than māyā and those who are free of it

बृहत्त्वात् - because it is more pervasive

बृंहणत्वात् च - and because it is more pervasive

अक्षरम् - Akṣara

ब्रह्म - Brahman

इति - as the aforementioned

उच्यते - is known

Akṣarabrahman is more pervasive than all of the jīvas, īśvaras, māyā, and those who are free of māyā. Therefore, it is known as 'Brahman'.[20] (39)

---

20 It is common practice in Saṃskṛta to define nouns based on the verbs from which they stem. The *Svāminārāyaṇa-siddhānta-sudhā* argues that the word 'Brahman' originates from either of the synonymous root verbs 'bṛha' and 'bṛhi' (Bhadreshdas 19), which the Pāṇinian Saṃskṛta tradition defines as 'vṛddhi', or 'growth' (Jha 31). The *Siddhānta-sudhā* then goes on to explain that Akṣarabrahman is larger in scope than the jīva, īśvara, and māyā, and so is correctly referred to as 'Brahman'.

तत्परः परमात्माऽस्ति परब्रह्मेति शब्दितः ।
शब्दसमयमाश्रित्य मुख्यार्थ उपवर्णितः ॥ ४० ॥

tatparaḥ paramātmā'sti parabrahmeti śabditaḥ,
śabdasamayamāśritya mukhyārtha upavarṇitaḥ.

पदच्छेदः - तत्परः, परमात्मा, अस्ति, परब्रह्म, इति, शब्दितः, शब्दसमयम्, आश्रित्य, मुख्यार्थः, उपवर्णितः ॥

अन्वयः

तत्परः - greater than this entity

परमात्मा - Paramātman

परब्रह्म - Parabrahman

इति - as

शब्दितः - called

अस्ति - is

शब्दसमयमम् - principles related to words and their interpretation

आश्रित्य - adhering to

मुख्यार्थः - the primary meaning

उपवर्णितः - has been explained.

Paramātman, who is greater than Akṣarabrahman, is identified as Parabrahman. The primary meaning of these words ['Akṣara' and 'Brahman'] have hence been etymologically explicated according to the principles of classical Indian hermeneutics. (40)

2.6 Akṣarabrahman's Virtues & Figure

Having explained the meaning of the terms 'Akṣara' and 'Brahman', the author now describes Akṣarabrahman's form and nature.

परस्माद् ब्रह्मणो भिन्नं तदेकाधीनतायुतम्।
नित्यमेकं गुणातीतं मायाधिपं च चेतनम्॥ ४१ ॥

parasmād brahmaṇo bhinnaṃ tadekādhīnatāyutam,
nityamekaṃ guṇātītaṃ māyādhipaṃ ca cetanam.

पदच्छेदः - परस्मात्, ब्रह्मणः, भिन्नम्, तदेकाधीनतायुतम्, नित्यम्, एकम्, गुणातीतम्, मायाधिपम्, च, चेतनम्॥

अन्वयः

(अक्षरब्रह्म) - Akṣarabrahman
परस्माद् ब्रह्मणः - from Parabrahman
भिन्नम् - distinct
(अस्ति) - is
तदेकाधीनतायुतम् - possesses dependancy only to it
नित्यम् - eternal
एकम् - unique
गुणातीतम् - guṇātīta
मायाधिपम् - māyā's controller
चेतनम् - sentient
च - and
(अस्ति) - is

Akṣarabrahman is distinct from Parabrahman and is dependent only upon Parabrahman.[21] It is eternal, unique, and guṇātīta; it is māyā's controller and is sentient. (41)

---

21 The *Svāminārāyaṇa-siddhānta-sudhā* eloquently discusses Akṣarabrahman's metaphysical identity as being above all but subordinate to Parabrahman on the basis of the Muṇḍakopaniṣad's seminal mantra, 'akṣarāt parataḥ paraḥ' and the *Bhagavadgītā*'s eighth and fifteenth cantos (Bhadreshdas 23-25, 41; 28-32).

श्रेयोऽनन्तगुणैर्युक्तं मायादोषविवर्जितम्।
बृहत्त्वात् सगुणं प्रोक्तं सूक्ष्मत्वान्निर्गुणं तथा॥ ४२॥

śreyo'nantaguṇairyuktaṃ māyādoṣavivarjitam,
bṛhattvāt saguṇaṃ proktaṃ sūkṣmatvānnirguṇaṃ tathā.

पदच्छेदः - श्रेयोऽनन्तगुणैः, युक्तम्, मायादोषविवर्जितम्, बृहत्त्वात्, सगुणम्, प्रोक्तम्, सूक्ष्मत्वात्, निर्गुणम्, तथा॥

अन्वयः

श्रेयोऽनन्तगुणैः - with infinite redemptive qualities

युक्तम् - is possessed

(अक्षरब्रह्म) - Akṣarabrahman

बृहत्त्वात् - due to persasiveness

सगुणम् - saguṇa

प्रोक्तम् - is known as

तथा - and

मायादोषविवर्जितम् - free of flaws that arise from māyā

(तदेव अक्षरब्रह्म) - this very Akṣarabrahman

सूक्ष्मत्वात् - due to subtleness

निर्गुणम् - nirguṇa

प्रोक्तम् - is known as

Akṣarabrahman is known as being saguṇa because it possesses infinite redemptive qualities and is pervasive. It is described as being nirguṇa, on the other hand, because it is subtle and free of flaws that arise from māyā.[22] (42)

22 'Guṇa' means quality. This verse explains that Akṣarabrahman is saguṇa (with qualities) and nirguṇa (without qualities), respectively, because 1) It possesses infinite redemptive qualities, such as bhakti, humility, and compassion, yet is free from flaws arising from māyā; and 2) It possesses the specific quality of pervasiveness when seen from the perspective of its omnipresence, yet does not appear to possess this quality when seen from the perspective of its subtle form.

उपादानं निमित्तं च तद्धि सर्जनकारणम्।
आधारो व्यापकं सृष्टेरन्तर्यामि नियामकम्॥ ४३॥

upādānaṃ nimittaṃ ca taddhi sarjanakāraṇam,
ādhāro vyāpakaṃ sṛṣṭerantaryāmi niyāmakam.

पदच्छेदः - उपादानम्, निमित्तम्, च, तद्, हि, सर्जनकारणम्, आधारः, व्यापकम्, सृष्टेः, अन्तर्यामि, नियामकम्॥

अन्वयः

तद् - it (Akṣarabrahman)

हि - certainly

उपादानम् - material

निमित्तं च - and efficient

सर्जनकारणम् - cause of creation

सृष्टेः - of creation

आधारः - sustainer

व्यापकम् - that which pervades

अन्तर्यामि - that which resides within

नियामकम् - that which controls

च - and

(अस्ति) - is

Akṣarabrahman is both the efficient and material cause of creation.[23] It also pervades and sustains creation. Furthermore, it resides within all as the controller. (43)

23 Indian philosophers often use the analogy of an earthen pot to describe material and efficient causes. The pot's material cause is the clay that forms the pot's raw substance; the potter who facilitates the pot's creation is the pot's efficient cause. Similarly, Akṣarabrahman is creation's material cause because it pervades and sustains; it is the efficient cause because it initiates the process of creation. It is important to note, however, that Akṣarabrahman serves in both of these capacities according to Parabrahman's will.

2.7 One Entity with Four Forms

Now, the four forms of Akṣarabrahman are enumerated. Namely, these four forms are the cidākāśa, the divine abode, the servant in the divine abode, and the manifest guru.

चतुर्धाऽवस्थितिर्ज्ञेया कार्यभेदान्न तत्त्वतः ।
मुक्तिसृष्टिलयाद्यर्थमेकस्यैवाऽक्षरस्य तु ॥ ४४ ॥

caturdhā'vasthitirjñeyā kāryabhedānna tattvataḥ,
muktisṛṣṭilayādyarthamekasyaivā'kṣarasya tu.

पदच्छेदः - चतुर्धा, अवस्थितिः, ज्ञेया, कार्यभेदात्, न, तत्त्वतः, मुक्तिसृष्टिलयाद्यर्थम्, एकस्य, एव, अक्षरस्य, तु ॥

अन्वयः

मुक्तिसृष्टिलयाद्यर्थम् - for liberation, creation, destruction, and other such tasks

एकस्य - of one

एव - indeed

अक्षरस्य - Akṣara

तु - indeed

कार्यभेदात् - due to variation in service roles

चतुर्धा - four

अवस्थितिः - forms

ज्ञेया - should be known

न - not

तत्त्वतः - ontologically

Akṣarabrahman is indeed only one, yet it appears in four forms. These forms do not reflect an ontological difference but merely signify the entity's various service roles, such as those it assumes in the processes of liberation, creation, and destruction. (44)

चिदाकाशस्तथा देशस्तद्देशस्थश्च सेवकः ।
गुरुर्ब्रह्मस्वरूपश्च चतस्रो ब्रह्मणो विधाः ॥ ४५ ॥

cidākāśastathā deśastaddeśasthaśca sevakaḥ,
gururbrahmasvarūpaśca catasro brahmaṇo vidhāḥ.

पदच्छेदः - चिदाकाशः, तथा, देशः, तद्देशस्थः, च, सेवकः, गुरुः, ब्रह्मस्वरूपः, च, चतस्रः, ब्रह्मणः, विधाः ॥

अन्वयः

चिदाकाशः - the cidākāśa
तथा - and
देशः - abode
तद्देशस्थः च - and within that abode
सेवकः - servant
ब्रह्मस्वरूपः च - and the brahmasvarūpa
गुरुः - guru
(इति) - thereby
ब्रह्मणः - Akṣarabrahman's
चतस्रः - four
विधाः - forms
(सन्ति) - are

Akṣarabrahman's four forms are the cidākāśa, the divine abode, the servant in that abode, and the brahmasvarūpa guru.[24] (45)

24 The *Svāminārāyaṇa-siddhānta-sudhā* discusses Akṣarabrahman's four forms at length through an edifying dialectic that provides about 300 references from the Prasthānatrayī, the larger Vedic canon, and the Vacanāmṛta (Bhadreshdas 47-84).

Of Akṣarabrahman's four forms, the author first explicates the cidākāśa, which pervades and sustains creation. His elucidation, in particular, makes note of the Upaniṣads' description of this form.

छान्दोग्ये दहराऽऽकाशश्चिदाकाशः प्रकीर्तितः ।
सकलहृद्गुहावर्ती यदन्तः पुरुषोत्तमः ॥ ४६ ॥

chāndogye daharā''kāśaścidākāśaḥ prakīrtitaḥ,
sakalahṛdguhāvartī yadantaḥ puruṣottamaḥ.

पदच्छेदः - छान्दोग्ये, दहराऽऽकाशः, चिदाकाशः, प्रकीर्तितः, सकलहृद्गुहावर्ती, यदन्तः, पुरुषोत्तमः ॥

अन्वयः

छान्दोग्ये - in the Chāndogya [Upaniṣad]

चिदाकाशः - the cidākāśa

दहराऽऽकाशः (इति) - as 'daharākāśa'

प्रकीर्तितः - is described as

सकलहृद्गुहावर्ती - that which resides in the hearts of all

यदन्तः च - and within which

पुरुषोत्तमः - Puruṣottama

(विराजते) - resides

The Chāndogyopaniṣad refers to Akṣarabrahman's cidākāśa form as 'daharākāśa'. It describes it as residing in the heart of every being and shows Puruṣottama as residing within it.[25] (46)

25 Chāndogyopaniṣad 8.1.1; Bhadreshdas, *Upaniṣat-svāminārāyaṇa-bhāṣyam*, Vol.3, 342–43.

तदेव याज्ञवल्क्योक्तौ गार्गीप्रश्नोत्तरे स्थितम्।
निखिललोककालादेर्ब्रह्माक्षरं प्रशासकम्॥ ४७॥

tadeva yājñavalkyoktau gārgīpraśnottare sthitam,
nikhilalokakāladerbrahmākṣaraṃ praśāsakam.

पदच्छेदः - तद्, एव, याज्ञवल्क्योक्तौ, गार्गीप्रश्नोत्तरे, स्थितम्, निखिललोककालादेः, ब्रह्माक्षरम्, प्रशासकम्॥

अन्वयः

तद् - this (Akṣarabrahman's cidākāśa form)

एव - itself

(बृहदारण्यके) - in the Bṛhadāraṇyakopaniṣad

गार्गीप्रश्नोत्तरे - in the answer to Gārgī's question

याज्ञवल्क्योक्तौ - in Yājñavalkya's words

स्थितम् - appears

(तत्र) - there

ब्रह्माक्षरम् - Akṣarabrahman

निखिललोककालादेः - of all of the realms, time, etc.

प्रशासकम् - the controller

(निरूपितम्) - is described as

This cidākāśa form of Akṣarabrahman is explained in Yājñavalkya's response to Gārgī's question [in the Bṛhadāraṇyakopaniṣad]. Akṣarabrahman is described there to be the controller of everything, including all realms and time.[26] (47)

26 Bṛhadāraṇyakopaniṣad 3.8.8-11; Bhadreshdas, *Upaniṣat-svāminārāyaṇa-bhāṣyam*, Vol.2, 190–99.

Akṣarabrahman appears in its second form as Paramātman's residence, which is known as Akṣaradhāman. The nature of this form is described in the following three verses.

ब्रह्मेशः सहजानन्दः स्वयं ब्रह्माऽक्षरं तथा।
मुक्ताश्च यत्र तिष्ठन्ति ह्यक्षरधाम कीर्तितम्॥ ४८॥

brahmeśaḥ sahajānandaḥ svayaṃ brahmā'kṣaraṃ tathā,
muktāśca yatra tiṣṭhanti hyakṣaradhāma kīrtitam.

पदच्छेदः - ब्रह्मेशः, सहजानन्दः, स्वयम्, ब्रह्माऽक्षरम्, तथा, मुक्ताः, च, यत्र, तिष्ठन्ति, हि, अक्षरधाम, कीर्तितम्॥

अन्वयः

ब्रह्मेशः - the master of Akṣarabrahman

सहजानन्दः - Sahajanand (Swaminarayan)

च - and

स्वयम् - itself

ब्रह्माऽक्षरम् - Akṣarabrahman

तथा - and

मुक्ताः - liberated beings

यत्र - where

तिष्ठन्ति - reside

(तद्) - that

हि - indeed

अक्षरधाम - Akṣaradhāman

कीर्तितम् - is known as

The residence of the liberated beings, of Akṣarabrahman itself, and of Swaminarayan, who is the master of Akṣarabrahman, is indeed known as Akṣaradhāman. (48)

मनुष्याकारतस्तद्धि साकृतिकं भवेत् सदा।
तस्य चतुर्षु पार्श्वेषु नैकब्रह्माण्डसंस्थितिः ॥ ४९ ॥

manuṣyākāratastaddhi sākṛtikaṃ bhavet sadā,
tasya catuḥṣu pārśveṣu naikabrahmāṇḍasaṃsthitiḥ.

पदच्छेदः - मनुष्याकारतः, तत्, हि, साकृतिकम्, भवेत्, सदा, तस्य, चतुर्षु, पार्श्वेषु, नैकब्रह्माण्डसंस्थितिः ॥

अन्वयः

तत् - that

हि - certainly

सदा - always

मनुष्याकारतः - by being that which possesses a human figure

साकृतिकम् - with a form

भवेत् - is

तस्य - its

चतुर्षु - in [all] four

पार्श्वेषु - sides

नैकब्रह्माण्डसंस्थितिः - the existence of countless brahmāṇḍas[31]

By possessing a human figure, it is forever sākāra (with form). Countless brahmāṇḍas[27] reside on all four of its sides.[28] (49)

---

27 A unit of creation.

28 The *Svāminārāyaṇa-siddhānta-sudhā* establishes that Akṣaradhāman possesses a definite form and is thus an actual place by referring to Prasthānatrayī verses that describe this abode using words such as 'loka' (Praśnopaniṣad 1.15), 'dhāman' (Muṇḍakopaniṣad 3.2.4, *Gītā* 8.21, 15.6), 'pada' (*Gītā* 8.11, 15.4-5), 'sthāna' (*Gītā* 8.28), and 'sadman' (Kaṭhopaniṣad, 2.14) (Bhadreshdas 57-60).

नास्त्यपरः परो लोको ह्यस्माद्ध्यक्षरधामतः।
यतो विराजते नित्यम् अत्र पराऽक्षरात् परः॥ ५०॥

nāstyaparaḥ paro loko hyasmāddhyakṣaradhāmataḥ,
yato virājate nityam atra parā'kṣarāt paraḥ.

पदच्छेदः - नास्ति, अपरः, परः, लोकः, हि, अस्माद्, हि, अक्षरधामतः, यतः, विराजते, नित्यम्, अत्र, पराऽक्षरात्, परः॥

अन्वयः

अस्माद् - other than this
हि - indeed
अक्षरधामतः - Akṣaradhāman
परः - above
अपरः - other
लोकः - realm
हि - indeed
नास्ति - does not exist
यतः - because
अत्र - here
पराऽक्षरात् परः - that which is above Akṣarabrahman, which is above all
नित्यम् - eternally
विराजते - resides

There is no abode superior to this Akṣaradhāman. Indeed, Akṣaradhāman is supreme because that which is superior to the transcendent entity of Akṣarabrahman[29] eternally resides here. (50)

29 The phrase 'parā'kṣarāt paraḥ', which describes Parabrahman, is a direct reference to the term 'parātparaḥ', which appears in Praśnopaniṣad 5.5 and Muṇḍakopaniṣad 3.2.8 in reference to Parabrahman. Parabrahman is similarly described in Muṇḍakopaniṣad 2.1.2 as 'akṣarātparaḥ paraḥ' (Bhadreshdas, *Upaniṣat-svāminārāyaṇa-bhāṣyam*, Vol.1 218–19, 297–98, 258–61). See also verse 80 of the present text.

The author now describes Akṣarabrahman's third form, which acts as Paramātman's servant in the divine abode and is instrumental in initiating creation.

सहजानन्दसेवायां धाम्नि यद् राजते सदा।
साकृति चेतनं ह्येकं सर्वाङ्गदिव्यविग्रहम्॥ ५१ ॥

sahajānandasevāyāṃ dhāmni yad rājate sadā,
sākṛti cetanaṃ hyekaṃ sarvāṅgadivyavigraham.

पदच्छेदः - सहजानन्दसेवायाम्, धाम्नि, यद्, राजते, सदा, साकृति, चेतनम्, हि, एकम्, सर्वाङ्गदिव्यविग्रहम्॥

अन्वयः

धाम्नि - in Akṣaradhāman

सदा - always

सहजानन्दसेवायाम् - in Sahajanand's (Swaminarayan's) service

यद् - which

राजते - resides

(तत्) - that

(अक्षरब्रह्मणः) - Akṣarabrahman's

(सेवकरूपम्) - servant form

सर्वाङ्गदिव्यविग्रहम् - that which has a body whose every part is divine

साकृति - that which possesses a human figure

चेतनम् - that which is sentient

(च) - and

एकम् - that which is unique

हि - certainly

Within Akṣaradhāman is the form of Akṣarabrahman that eternally serves Swaminarayan. It is sentient, unique, and possesses a human figure whose every part is divine. (51)

सिसृक्षुः सहजानन्दः प्रथमतस्तदीक्षते।
तदपि मुक्तवृन्दं च ह्येवं तत् सृष्टिकारणम्॥ ५२॥

sisṛkṣuḥ sahajānandaḥ prathamatastadīkṣate,
tadapi muktavṛndaṃ ca hyevaṃ tat sṛṣṭikāraṇam.

पदच्छेदः - सिसृक्षुः, सहजानन्दः, प्रथमतः, तत्, ईक्षते, तत्, अपि, मुक्तवृन्दम्, च, हि, एवम्, तत्, सृष्टिकारणम्॥

अन्वयः

सिसृक्षुः - wishing to create

सहजानन्दः - Sahajanand (Swaminarayan)

प्रथमतः - at first (before creation)

तत् - at it (this form of Akṣarabrahman)

ईक्षते - looks

च - and

तत् - that (this form of Akṣarabrahman)

अपि - in turn

मुक्तवृन्दम् - at the multitude of liberated beings

(ईक्षते) - looks

एवम् - in this way

हि - indeed

तत् - it (Akṣarabrahman)

सृष्टिकारणम् - the cause of creation

(विद्यते) - is

When Swaminarayan wishes to create, he first looks towards this form of Akṣarabrahman. In turn, Akṣarabrahman looks towards the multitude of liberated beings [and selects one of these beings to be responsible for creation]. In this way, indeed, Akṣarabrahman plays a causal role in the process of cosmogenesis. (52)

Akṣarabrahman's fourth form is the guru, who is always manifest on earth. Upon arguing that the previous three forms are difficult to attain, the author praises this fourth form by saying that it is accessible to all. He then expands on its nature and its role in spiritual praxis.

गुरुरक्षरब्रह्मैव दिव्यो दिव्यतनोर्धरः ।
नारायणस्वरूपं च सम्प्रदायाऽभिरक्षकः ॥ ५३ ॥

gururakṣarabrahmaiva divyo divyatanordharaḥ,
nārāyaṇasvarūpaṃ ca sampradāyā'bhirakṣakaḥ.

पदच्छेदः - गुरुः, अक्षरब्रह्म, एव, दिव्यः, दिव्यतनोः, धरः, नारायणस्वरूपम्, च, सम्प्रदायाऽभिरक्षकः ॥

अन्वयः

अक्षरब्रह्म - Akṣarabrahman

एव - indeed

दिव्यः - divine

गुरुः - the guru

(अस्ति) - is

दिव्यतनोः - of a divine body

धरः - ḥe who takes upon

नारायणस्वरूपम् - the form of Nārāyaṇa

सम्प्रदायाऽभिरक्षकः च - and the guardian of the sampradāya

(अस्तिः) - is

This very entity of Akṣarabrahman takes upon a sacred, human form and serves as the holy guru. He is the form of Nārāyaṇa and the guardian of the sampradāya.[30] (53)

30 The guru protects and fosters the sampradāya's traditions and is thus described as its guardian.

परमात्मा तु तत्रैव सम्यक् सदा विराजते।
स्वप्राकट्याऽनुभूत्यर्थं नृणां भक्ताऽनुकम्पया ॥ ५४ ॥

paramātmā tu tatraiva samyak sadā virājate,
svaprākaṭyā'nubhūtyartham nṛṇām bhaktā'nukampayā.

पदच्छेदः - परमात्मा, तु, तत्र, एव, सम्यक्, सदा, विराजते, स्वप्राकट्याऽनुभूत्यर्थम्, नृणाम्, भक्ताऽनुकम्पया ॥

अन्वयः

परमात्मा - Paramātman

भक्ताऽनुकम्पया - out of compassion for devotees

नृणाम् - people's

स्वप्राकट्यानुभूत्यर्थं - for the experience of his manifestation

(च) - and

तु - indeed

तत्र - there (within the Akṣarabrahman guru)

एव - certainly

सम्यक् - entirely

सदा - eternally

विराजते - resides

Out of compassion for devotees, Paramātman indeed resides in the Akṣarabrahman guru entirely and eternally, enabling people to experience his manifestation. (54)

यथा ब्रह्मगुरौ वासः स्वामिनारायणप्रभोः ।
नैवाऽन्यत्र तथा क्वापि पात्राणां तारतम्यतः ॥ ५५ ॥

yathā brahmagurau vāsaḥ svāminārāyaṇaprabhoḥ,
naivā'nyatra tathā kvāpi pātrāṇāṃ tāratamyataḥ.

पदच्छेदः - यथा, ब्रह्मगुरौ, वासः, स्वामिनारायणप्रभोः, न, एव, अन्यत्र, तथा, क्व, अपि, पात्राणाम्, तारतम्यतः ॥

अन्वयः

पात्राणाम् - of vessels

तारतम्यतः - due to gradation

यथा - the way in which

ब्रह्मगुरौ - in the Akṣarabrahman guru

स्वामिनारायणप्रभोः - Bhagwan Swaminarayan's

वासः - presence

तथा - in the same way

न - not

एव - indeed

क्वापि अन्यत्र - anywhere else

(भवति) - occurs

Bhagwan Swaminarayan does not reside anywhere else as he does in the Akṣarabrahman guru. This is because of the gradation inherent in sentient beings.[31] (55)

31 Aside from Parabrahman, Akṣarabrahman is the foremost ontological entity. It has also been eternally free of māyā and thus stands alongside Parabrahman as the purest entity. Due to these and other reasons, Parabrahman is most fully present in Akṣarabrahman (Vacanāmṛta GP-41; Swaminarayan 73–76).

नारायणस्वरूपत्वाद् ध्येयो ब्रह्माऽक्षरं गुरुः।
नित्यमास्ते यतस्तस्मिन् सम्यङ्नारायणो हरिः॥ ५६॥

nārāyaṇasvarūpatvād dhyeyo brahmā'kṣaraṃ guruḥ,
nityamāste yatastasmin samyaṅnārāyaṇo hariḥ.

पदच्छेदः - नारायणस्वरूपत्वात्, ध्येयः, ब्रह्माऽक्षरम्, गुरुः, नित्यम्, आस्ते, यतः, तस्मिन्, सम्यक्, नारायणः, हरिः॥

अन्वयः

यतः - because

नारायणः हरिः - Nārāyaṇa Hari (Bhagwan Swaminarayan)

तस्मिन् (गुरौ) - within the guru

नित्यम् - eternally

सम्यग् - entirely

आस्ते - resides

नारायणस्वरूपत्वाद् - as the form of Nārāyaṇa

ब्रह्माऽक्षरम् - Akṣarabrahman

गुरुः - the guru

ध्येयः - is worthy of being meditated upon.

Parabrahman Swaminarayan, in his entirety, eternally resides within the Akṣarabrahman guru.[32] Hence, this guru is the form of Nārāyaṇa and is thus worthy of being meditated upon.[33] (56)

32 See verse 72.
33 Vacanāmṛta V-5; Swaminarayan 506.

ब्रह्म मानवरूपेण जायत इति बुध्यते।
आदर्शं तन्मुमुक्षूणां जीवनवर्तनादिषु॥ ५७॥

brahma mānavarūpeṇa jāyata iti budhyate,
ādarśaṃ tanmumukṣūṇāṃ jīvanavartanādiṣu.

पदच्छेद: - ब्रह्म, मानवरूपेण, जायते, इति, बुध्यते, आदर्शम्, तत्, मुमुक्षूणाम्, जीवनवर्तनादिषु॥

अन्वय:

ब्रह्म - Akṣarabrahman

मानवरूपेण - by way of a human form

जायते - is born

इति - thus

बुध्यते - is known

तत् - it (Akṣarabrahman)

जीवनवर्तनादिषु - in matters related to lifestyle and actions

मुमुक्षूणाम् - for spiritual seekers

आदर्शम् - an ideal

(भवति) - is

Akṣarabrahman is thus known to be born in human form;[34] through this form, Akṣarabrahman's lifestyle and actions serve as an ideal for spiritual seekers.[35] (57)

34 Vacanāmṛta GP-71; Swaminarayan 141–45.

35 Vacanāmṛta GP-67; Swaminarayan 132–33.

जन्म कर्म सदा दिव्यमक्षराधिपतेर्यथा।
तथैव तु विजानीयाद् ब्रह्माऽक्षरगुरोरिह॥ ५८॥

janma karma sadā divyamakṣarādhipateryathā,
tathaiva tu vijānīyād brahmā'kṣaraguroriha.

पदच्छेदः - जन्म, कर्म, सदा, दिव्यम्, अक्षराधिपतेः, यथा, तथा, एव, तु, विजानीयात्, ब्रह्माऽक्षरगुरोः, इह॥

अन्वयः

यथा - Just as

अक्षराधिपतेः - the ruler of Akṣara's

जन्म - birth

कर्म (च) - and actions

सदा - eternally

दिव्यम् - divine

तथा - in the same way

एव - indeed

इह - here (on earth)

ब्रह्माऽक्षरगुरोः - the Akṣarabrahman guru's

तु - certainly

विजानीयात् - should be known

Just as the life and actions of Paramātman, the ruler of Akṣarabrahman, are known to be eternally divine, the same should be known about the life and actions of the Akṣarabrahman guru presently manifest on earth. (58)

2.8 Akṣarabrahman's Prevalence in the Śāstras

तादृगुपनिषन्नास्ति गीताऽध्यायो न विद्यते।
अध्यायो ब्रह्मसूत्रे च प्रकरणं वचोऽमृते॥ ५९॥

ब्रह्माऽक्षरस्य दिव्यस्य यद्धि योगं विना भवेत्।
ब्रह्माऽतो संस्मरेन्नित्यं ब्रह्मभावाय भक्तये॥ ६०॥

tādṛgupaniṣannāsti gītā'dhyāyo na vidyate,
adhyāyo brahmasūtre ca prakaraṇaṃ vaco'mṛte.

brahmā'kṣarasya divyasya yaddhi yogaṃ vinā bhavet,
brahmā'to saṃsmarennityaṃ brahmabhāvāya bhaktaye.

पदच्छेदः - तादृक्, उपनिषत्, न, अस्ति, गीताऽध्यायः, न, विद्यते, अध्यायः, ब्रह्मसूत्रे, च, प्रकरणम्, वचोऽमृते॥ ब्रह्माऽक्षरस्य, दिव्यस्य, यद्, हि, योगम्, विना, भवेत्, ब्रह्म, अतः, संस्मरेत्, नित्यम्, ब्रह्मभावाय, भक्तये॥

अन्वयः

दिव्यस्य ब्रह्माऽक्षरस्य - of the divine Akṣarabrahman

यत् - that which

हि - indeed

योगम् - contact

विना - without

तादृक् - such

उपनिषत् - an Upaniṣad

न अस्ति - does not exist

गीताऽध्यायः - a canto of the *Gītā*

न विद्यते - does not exist

ब्रह्मसूत्रे - in the *Brahmasūtra*

अध्यायः - a chapter

(न विद्यते) - does not exist

वचोऽमृते च - and in the Vacanāmṛta

प्रकरणम् - a chapter

(न विद्यते) - does not exist

अतः - therefore

ब्रह्मभावाय - for attaining brahmabhāva

भक्तये (च) - and for bhakti
ब्रह्म - on Akṣarabrahman
नित्यम् - incessantly
संस्मरेत् - one should meditate

There is not one Upaniṣad or chapter of the *Gītā*, *Brahmasūtra*, or Vacanāmṛta that does not relate to the glory of the divine Akṣarabrahman. Thus, for attaining bhakti and brahmabhāva, one should incessantly meditate on Akṣarabrahman. (59-60)

एवं परब्रह्मस्वामिनारायणप्रबोधित-ब्रह्मस्वरूपगुणातीतगुरुपरम्परोपबृंहित-
ब्रह्मविद्यालक्षणाऽक्षरपुरुषोत्तमदर्शनप्रतिपादके
साधुभद्रेशदासविरचिते
स्वामिनारायणसिद्धान्तसुधाऽऽख्ये शास्त्रेऽस्मिन्
समाप्तमक्षरब्रह्मधारा नाम
द्वितीयं प्रकरणम् ॥

In this way ends the second chapter, known as the 'Akṣarabrahma-dhārā', of Sadhu Bhadreshdas' *Svāminārāyaṇa-siddhānta-sudhā*, a text that substantiates the Akṣara-Puruṣottama Darśana, which is characterised as brahmavidyā, was taught by Parabrahman Swaminarayan, and has been fostered by the lineage of brahmasvarūpa, guṇātīta gurus.

Chapter 3

Parabrahma-dhārā

3.1 Introduction

Knowledge of Akṣarabrahman is necessary for one who wishes to understand Parabrahman and secure liberation. Having described Akṣarabrahman's form and significance in the previous chapter, the author thus goes on to elaborate upon Parabrahman. He first describes Parabrahman's virtues and form, explaining that Parabrahman is omniscient, compassionate, above māyā, unique, and unmatchable. He also puts forth that Parabrahman is eternally served by Akṣarabrahman and the released beings in his divine abode, Akṣaradhāman. He then says that Parabrahman is also pervasive, despite being eternally present in his abode.

The author further discusses Parabrahman's role in creation, describing Parabrahman as the material and efficient cause of all and the entity that gifts living beings with life and the ability to know, desire, and act. He also describes Parabrahman as the entity that grants beings the fruits of their karma.

Bhadreśhdas then explicates the Akṣara-Puruṣottama Darśana's philosophy of divine manifestation, saying that this very Parabrahman comes to earth as Swaminarayan himself to liberate people from the cycle of births and deaths. The author further declares the darśana's teaching that this very entity of Parabrahman Swaminarayan alone is worthy of being offered the highest form of upāsanā.

Thereafter, the author presents an intriguing dialectic wherein he first posits that Parabrahman, indeed, possesses a human form. He then answers prima facie claims that put forth Upaniṣadic verses to show Parabrahman to be formless. Specifically, he says that such statements that appear in the śāstras are not blanket claims that negate Parabrahman's form altogether, but that they are mere negations of Parabrahman having a worldly form.

He then goes on to describe Parabrahman's pre-eminence. He further says that Bhagwan Swaminarayan stays present on earth through the lineage of Akṣarabrahman gurus after his passing and that divyabhāva (an understanding of inherent divinity) in his manifest form leads to liberation.

In this way, the 'Parabrahma-dhārā' examines the nature of Parabrahman's form and manifestation and considers its implications.

3.2 Benediction

The Parabrahma-dhārā commences with obeisance to Parabrahman Bhagwan Swaminarayan. While adhering to the tradition of recalling God's name at the commencement of an undertaking, this benediction also explains why the ultimate entity is known by the name of Swaminarayan.

सहितः स्वामिना नित्यमास्ते नारायणो हरिः ।
स्वामिनारायणस्तस्मात् कीर्त्यते समुपास्यते ॥ ६१ ॥

sahitaḥ svāminā nityamāste nārāyaṇo hariḥ,
svāminārāyaṇastasmāt kīrtyate samupāsyate.

पदच्छेदः - सहितः, स्वामिना, नित्यम्, आस्ते, नारायणः, हरिः, स्वामिनारायणः, तस्मात्, कीर्त्यते, समुपास्यते ॥

अन्वयः

नारायणः - Nārāyaṇa

हरिः - Hari

स्वामिना सहितः - with Svāmī

नित्यम् - eternally

आस्ते - presides

तस्मात् - therefore

स्वामिनारायणः - Swaminarayan

कीर्त्यते - is known as

समुपास्यते - is worshipped

Bhagavān Nārāyaṇa (Parabrahman Swaminarayan) eternally presides along with Svāmī (Akṣarabrahman). Thus, he is known and worshipped as 'Swaminarayan'.[36] (61)

36 The Akṣara-Puruṣottama Darśana reads the name 'Swaminarayan', as well as the Swaminarayan mantra, according to the madhyamapadalopī compound formation, which is embedded with the instrumental tatpuruṣa compound, according to Kātyāyana vārtika 1310 and Pāṇini sūtra 2.1.13 (Govindācārya 105, 99). When the name is divided into its constituent parts, it reads as such: svāminā sahito nārāyaṇa iti svāminārāyaṇaḥ.

3.3 Parabrahman's Divine Virtues & Figure

परमात्मा परं ब्रह्म सर्वेश्वरेश्वरो हरिः।
नारायणश्च सर्वज्ञः कृपालुः पुरुषोत्तमः ॥ ६२ ॥

paramātmā paraṃ brahma sarveśvareśvaro hariḥ,
nārāyaṇaśca sarvajñaḥ kṛpāluḥ puruṣottamaḥ.

पदच्छेदः - परमात्मा, परम्, ब्रह्म, सर्वेश्वरेश्वरः, हरिः, नारायणः, च, सर्वज्ञः, कृपालुः, पुरुषोत्तमः ॥

अन्वयः

परं ब्रह्म - Parabrahman

परमात्मा - Paramātman

पुरुषोत्तमः - Puruṣottama

नारायणः - Nārāyaṇa

हरिः - Hari

सर्वेश्वरेश्वरः - Sarveśvareś-vara

सर्वज्ञः - the all-knower

कृपालुः - compassionate

च - and

(वर्तते) - is

Parabrahman is also known as Paramātman, Puruṣottama, Nārāyaṇa, Hari, Sarveśvareśvara and the compassionate, all-knower.[37] (62)

37 The terms used in this verse to describe Parabrahman, rooted in the Prasthānatrayī, reflect much about the Akṣara-Puruṣottama Darśana's beliefs about the ultimate entity and the darśana's metaphysics. For instance, the term 'Parabrahman', which appears in Praśnopaniṣad 5.2, indicates God's distinctness from and superiority to Akṣarabrahman; 'Paramātman', which is seen in *Gītā* 15.17, suggests that God is distinct from and superior to the ātman; 'Puruṣottama', appearing in *Gītā* 15.18, suggests that he is distinct from and superior to the jīva, īśvara, and Akṣarabrahman, which the *Gītā* describes as puruṣas; and 'Sarveśvareśvara', which stems from Śvetāśvataropaniṣad 6.7, indicates that he is distinct from and superior the īśvaras. By elucidating Parabrahman in this way, the author makes note of both Parabrahman's supremacy and the Akṣara-Puruṣottama Darśana's teaching of four ontologically distinct sentient entities.

मायाऽतीतश्च निर्दोषः साकृतिर्मानवाऽऽकृतिः ।
नित्यः सर्वसमुत्कृष्ट एकोऽयं नैव तत्समः ॥ ६३ ॥

māyā'tītaśca nirdoṣaḥ sākṛtirmānavā''kṛtiḥ,
nityaḥ sarvasamutkṛṣṭa eko'yaṃ naiva tatsamaḥ.

पदच्छेदः - मायाऽतीतः, च, निर्दोषः, साकृतिः, मानवाऽऽकृतिः, नित्यः, सर्वसमुत्कृष्टः, एकः, अयम्, न, एव, तत्समः ॥

अन्वयः

अयम् (परमात्मा) - this here Paramātman

मायाऽतीतः - one who is above māyā

निर्दोषः - one who is free of flaws

साकृतिः - one who possesses a form

मानवाऽऽकृतिः - one who is of human form

च - and

नित्यः - one who is eternal

एकः - one who is unique

एव - indeed

सर्वसमुत्कृष्टः - one who is superior to all

तत्समः - one who is equal to him

न (अस्ति) - does not exist

This here Paramātman is above māyā, is untouched by flaws, possesses a human form, and is eternal. He is unique and greatly superior to all; no one is equal to him. (63)

दिव्यगुणविशिष्टोऽयं मायिकगुणवर्जितः।
अन्तर्यामी सर्वकर्ता गुणाऽतीतो नियामकः॥ ६४॥

divyaguṇaviśiṣṭo'yaṃ māyikaguṇavarjitaḥ,
antaryāmī sarvakartā guṇā'tīto niyāmakaḥ.

पदच्छेदः - दिव्यगुणविशिष्टः, अयम्, मायिकगुणवर्जितः, अन्तर्यामी, सर्वकर्ता, गुणाऽतीतः, नियामकः॥

अन्वयः

अयम् (परमात्मा) - This here Paramātman

दिव्यगुणविशिष्टः - one who possesses divine virtues

मायिकगुणवर्जितः - one who is free of māyic flaws

अन्तर्यामी - one who resides in all[38]

सर्वकर्ता - one who is the omniagent

गुणाऽतीतः - one who is above māyā's qualities

नियामकः - one who governs

Paramātman possesses divine virtues and is free of worldly attributes. He resides within all,[39] is the omniagent, and is beyond māyā. He is the controller of all. (64)

---

38 The word antaryāmīn, which is formed from the indeclinable 'antar' and the root verb 'yama', denotes both pervasiveness and governance. Paramātman is described at length in this way and using these terms in Bṛhadāraṇyakopaniṣad 3.7.1-23 (Bhadreshdas, *Upaniṣat-svāminārāyaṇa-bhāṣyam*, Vol.2, 177–86).

मूर्तिमद्ब्रह्मणा नित्यं मुक्तैस्तद्भावभावितैः ।
सेव्यते दासभावेन ह्यक्षरधामसंस्थितः ॥ ६५ ॥

mūrtimadbrahmaṇā nityaṃ muktaistadbhāvabhāvitaiḥ,
sevyate dāsabhāvena hyakṣaradhāma-saṃsthitaḥ.

पदच्छेदः - मूर्तिमद्ब्रह्मणा, नित्यम्, मुक्तैः, तद्भावभावितैः, सेव्यते, दासभावेन, हि, अक्षरधामसंस्थितः ॥

अन्वयः

अक्षरधामसंस्थितः - that which resides in Akṣaradhāman

(परमात्मा) - Paramātman

नित्यम् - eternally

मूर्तिमद्ब्रह्मणा - by the personal form of Akṣarabrahman

तद्भावभावितैः मुक्तैः (च) - and by those liberated beings who have attained qualitative oneness with it (i.e. with Akṣarabrahman)

दासभावेन - humbly

हि - indeed

सेव्यते - is served

In Akṣaradhāman, Paramātman is humbly served by the personal form of Akṣarabrahman and the countless liberated beings that have attained qualitative oneness with Akṣarabrahman. (65)

उपादानं निमित्तं च कारणं जगतो मतः।
सर्वाधारः स्वतन्त्रश्च कर्ता हर्ता नियामकः॥ ६६ ॥

upādānaṃ nimittaṃ ca kāraṇaṃ jagato mataḥ,
sarvādhāraḥ svatantraśca kartā hartā niyāmakaḥ.

पदच्छेदः - उपादानम्, निमित्तम्, च, कारणम्, जगतः, मतः, सर्वाधारः, स्वतन्त्रः, च, कर्ता, हर्ता, नियामकः॥

अन्वयः

(परमात्मा) - Paramātman

जगतः - creation's

उपादानम् - material

निमित्तं च - and efficient[40]

कारणम् - cause

मतः - is known as

सर्वाधारः - one who is the sustainer of all

स्वतन्त्रः - one who is independent

कर्ता - the creator

हर्ता - the destroyer

नियामकः च - and the controller

He is known as creation's material and efficient cause.[39] He sustains all and is the creator, destroyer, and controller. (66)

39 See footnote 23 for an explanation of material and efficient causes.

As part of his discussion of Parabrahman's form and nature, the author explains Parabrahman's pervasive (anvaya) and distinct (vyatireka) forms. In particular, he says that the pervasive form is present everywhere, whereas the distinct form resides specifically in Akṣaradhāman, the divine abode.

स्वधामस्थित एवाऽयं सकलाऽन्विततां गतः।
व्यतिरिक्तोऽन्वितोऽपीह स्वामिनारायणो हरिः॥ ६७॥

svadhāmasthita evā'yaṃ sakalā'nvitatāṃ gataḥ,
vyatirikto'nvito'pīha svāminārāyaṇo hariḥ.

पदच्छेदः - स्वधामस्थितः, एव, अयम्, सकलाऽन्विततताम्, गतः, व्यतिरिक्तः, अन्वितः, अपि, इह, स्वामिनारायणः, हरिः॥

अन्वयः

अयम् - This here

स्वामिनारायणः हरिः - Bhagwan Swaminarayàn

स्वधामस्थितः - one who resides in his sacred abode

एव - indeed

सकलाऽन्विततताम् - pervasiveness in all

गतः - enjoys

(पुनश्च) - moreover

अन्वितः - pervasive

अपि - although

इह - here (in the divine abode)

व्यतिरिक्तः - distinct

(प्रवर्तते) - is

Even while residing in his sacred abode, Bhagwan Swaminarayan pervades all. And while pervading creation, he remains distinct in his abode. (67)

मनुष्यादिजनेर्दाता सर्वकर्मफलप्रदः।
सर्वज्ञानक्रियेच्छानां शक्तेर्दाता दयाऽन्वितः॥ ६८॥

manuṣyādijanerdātā sarvakarmaphalapradaḥ,
sarvajñānakriyecchānāṃ śakterdātā dayā'nvitaḥ.

पदच्छेदः - मनुष्यादिजनेः, दाता, सर्वकर्मफलप्रदः, सर्वज्ञानक्रियेच्छानाम्, शक्तेः, दाता, दयाऽन्वितः॥

अन्वयः

दयाऽन्वितः - he who is compassionate

(परमात्मा) - Paramātman

मनुष्यादिजनेः - of birth to humans and other beings

दाता - the giver

सर्वकर्मफलप्रदः - one who is the giver of the fruits of all karma

सर्वज्ञानक्रियेच्छानां शक्तेः - of the power to know, act, and desire

दाता (च) - and the giver

The compassionate Paramātman grants birth to humans and other beings, gives of them the fruits of their karma, and bestows upon them the power to know, act, and desire. (68)

3.4 Manifestation as Swaminarayan

दिव्यसंकल्पमात्रेण नैकानामुद्दिधीर्षया।
सकलैश्वर्यसम्पन्नो धाम्नि सन्नेव जायते॥ ६९॥

divyasaṃkalpamātreṇa naikānāmuddidhīrṣayā,
sakalaiśvaryasampanno dhāmni sanneva jāyate.

<u>पदच्छेदः</u> - दिव्यसंकल्पमात्रेण, नैकानाम्, उद्दिधीर्षया, सकलैश्वर्यसम्पन्नः, धाम्नि, सन्, एव, जायते॥

<u>अन्वयः</u>

(परमात्मा) - Paramātman

नैकानाम् (आत्मनाम्) - of countless souls

उद्दिधीर्षया - through the desire to liberate

दिव्यसंकल्पमात्रेण - only by way of [his own] sacred wish

धाम्नि - in the divine abode

सन् - being

एव - indeed

सकलैश्वर्यसम्पन्नः - one who possesses all divine powers

जायते - takes birth

Paramātman comes to earth bearing all of his divine powers;[40] his descent occurs through his own sacred wish to liberate countless beings.[41] All the while, he continues to reside in his divine abode. (69)

---

40 Bhadreshdas' statement that Paramātman comes to earth bearing all his divine virtues is a direct reference to a number of Vacanāmṛta discourses, such as GP-71, GA-31 (Swaminarayan 141–45, 610–12), which express that Paramātman does not become lesser by taking upon a 'human' form. See also verse 84 of the present text.

41 By positing that Paramātman takes birth independently, this verse counters the prima facie view that Paramātman is born due to karma.

स एव सहजानन्दः स्वामिनारायणो हरिः।
परमात्मा परं ब्रह्म भक्तिजो धर्मनन्दनः॥ ७०॥

sa eva sahajānandaḥ svāminārāyaṇo hariḥ,
paramātmā paraṃ brahma bhaktijo dharmanandanaḥ.

<u>पदच्छेदः</u> - सः, एव, सहजानन्दः, स्वामिनारायणः, हरिः, परमात्मा, परम्, ब्रह्म, भक्तिजः, धर्मनन्दनः॥

<u>अन्वयः</u>

सः - this

एव - very

परं ब्रह्म - Parabrahman

परमात्मा - Paramātman

भक्तिजः - the son of Bhakti

धर्मनन्दनः - the giver of joy to Dharma

स्वामिनारायणः हरिः - Bhagwan Swaminarayan

सहजानन्दः - Sahajanand

(अस्ति) - is

This very Parabrahman Paramātman is Bhagwan Swaminarayan, or Sahajanand Swami, the son of Bhakti and Dharma.[42] (70)

42 See footnote 3 under verse 2

स एव परमोपास्यो भजनीयश्च भावतः।
जप्यश्चाऽऽश्रयणीयश्च कीर्तनीयश्च सर्वदा॥ ७१ ॥

sa eva paramopāsyo bhajanīyaśca bhāvataḥ,
japyaścā''śrayaṇīyaśca kīrtanīyaśca sarvadā.

पदच्छेदः - सः, एव, परमोपास्यः, भजनीयः, च, भावतः, जप्यः, च, आश्रयणीयः, च, कीर्तनीयः, च, सर्वदा॥

अन्वयः

सः - he

एव - alone

परमोपास्यः - is worthy of being offered supreme upāsanā

भावतः च - and out of passion

भजनीयः - worthy of being worshipped

सर्वदा - for all times

कीर्तनीयः च - and worthy of being praised

जप्यः च - and worthy of being chanted

आश्रयणीयः च - and worthy of being gone to for shelter

He alone is worthy of being offered supreme upāsanā, passionate worship, and everlasting praise. His name alone is worthy of being chanted. He alone is worthy of being the ultimate refuge.[43] (71)

43 Singular devotion, or avyabhicāriṇi bhakti, is imperative to the Akṣara-Puruṣottama Darśana's orthopraxy, as expressed in the *Svāminārāyaṇa-siddhānta-sudhā* (Bhadreshdas 352-53). Swaminarayan explains this concept in the Vacanāmṛta by saying that a devotee should remain loyal to their iṣṭadeva just as a faithful wife, whom he calls a pativratā strī, is singularly dedicated to her partner. He adds, however, that a devotee who is loyal to one iṣṭadeva should still offer obeisance to other deities and should disparage none (L-11, GM-19, GA-16, 38; Swaminarayan 290, 401–02, 577–78, 627).

Verses 69-70 explained that Parabrahman manifested as Swaminarayan and that he alone is worthy of worship. The Akṣara-Puruṣottama Darśana also teaches, however, that Parabrahman stays on earth perennially even after Swaminarayan's passing. This eternal manifestation occurs through the Akṣarabrahman guru, as described below.

स एव प्रकटो नित्यं प्रत्यक्षे ब्रह्मणि गुरौ।
सहितः सकलैश्वर्यैः सम्यगानन्ददायकः॥ ७२॥

sa eva prakaṭo nityaṃ pratyakṣe brahmaṇi gurau,
sahitaḥ sakalaiśvaryaiḥ samyagānandadāyakaḥ.

पदच्छेदः - सः, एव, प्रकटः, नित्यम्, प्रत्यक्षे, ब्रह्मणि, गुरौ, सहितः, सकलैश्वर्यैः, सम्यक्, आनन्ददायकः॥

अन्वयः

सः - he

एव - himself

सम्यक् - in every way

आनन्ददायकः - the giver of bliss

सकलैश्वर्यैः सहितः - along with all of his divine virtues

प्रत्यक्षे ब्रह्मणि गुरौ - in the manifest, Akṣarabrahman guru

नित्यम् - eternally

प्रकटः - is manifest

The giver of absolute bliss; Parabrahman Swaminarayan himself is eternally present on earth along with all of his divine virtues through the manifest, Akṣarabrahman guru.[44] (72)

---

44 See also verses 54-6 in Chapter 2.

3.5 Premise for Creation

The author now explains that Paramātman creates the universes to engender liberation.

कल्याणं परमं भूयान्नैकजीवेश्वराऽऽत्मनाम्।
इदमेकं कृपालोस्तु सृष्टौ प्रयोजनं मतम्॥ ७३॥

kalyāṇaṃ paramaṃ bhūyānnaikajīveśvarā"tmanām,
idamekaṃ kṛpālostu sṛṣṭau prayojanaṃ matam.

पदच्छेदः - कल्याणम्, परमम्, भूयात्, नैकजीवेश्वराऽऽत्मनाम्, इदम्, एकम्, कृपालोः, तु, सृष्टौ, प्रयोजनम्, मतम्॥

अन्वयः

कृपालोः (परमात्मनः) - the compassionate Paramātman's

तु - indeed

सृष्टौ - in creation

इदम् - this

एकम् - one

प्रयोजनम् - purpose

मतम् - is understood

(यत्) - that

नैकजीवेश्वराऽऽत्मनाम् - of countless jīvas and īśvaras

परमम् - ultimate

कल्याणम् - liberation

भूयात् - may occur

The benevolent Paramātman's only purpose in creating the universe is to grant ultimate liberation to countless jīvas and īśvaras. (73)

3.6 Parabrahman's Sacred Form

The author now explicates Paramātman's eternal, human form. He also reconciles this view with references that seem to describe Paramātman as formless by saying that such verses merely refute the position that Paramātman's form is māyic.

साकृतिरेव कर्ताऽयं साकृतिर्व्यापको मतः।
साकृतिरेव शास्ता स नित्यं साकृतिको हरिः ॥ ७४ ॥

sākṛtireva kartā'yaṃ sākṛtirvyāpako mataḥ,
sākṛtireva śāstā sa nityaṃ sākṛtiko hariḥ.

पदच्छेदः - साकृतिः, एव, कर्ता, अयम्, साकृतिः, व्यापकः, मतः, साकृतिः, एव, शास्ता, सः, नित्यम्, साकृतिकः, हरिः ॥

अन्वयः

अयं हरिः - this very Paramātman

साकृतिः - one with a form

(सन्) एव - indeed being

कर्ता (अस्ति) - is the omniagent

(अयम्) - this entity

साकृतिः - one who has a form

(सन् एव) - indeed being

व्यापकः - pervasive

मतः - is known as

साकृतिः - that with a form

(सन्) एव - indeed being

शास्ता (अस्ति) - is the controller

(एवम्) - in this way

सः - this very

नित्यम् - eternally

साकृतिकः (अस्ति) - is one with a form

Paramātman serves in his capacity as the omniagent while having a definite form. He also pervades while possessing a definite form and controls all, again, while possessing a definite form. In this way, he eternally possesses a definite form. (74)

यश्च करणरूपादेर्निषेधः श्रूयते श्रुतौ।
मायिकस्यैव स ज्ञेयो दिव्यस्य तत्र रूपणात्॥ ७५॥

yaśca karaṇarūpādernisedhaḥ śrūyate śrutau,
māyikasyaiva sa jñeyo divyasya tatra rūpaṇāt.

पदच्छेदः - यः, च, करणरूपादेः, निषेधः, श्रूयते, श्रुतौ, मायिकस्य, एव, सः, ज्ञेयः, दिव्यस्य, तत्र, रूपणात्॥

अन्वयः

यः च - and that which

श्रुतौ - in the śrutis

(परमात्मनः) - Paramātman's

करणरूपादेः - of the sense organs, physical form, etc.

निषेधः - negation

श्रूयते - is heard

सः (निषेधः) - this negation

मायिकस्य (करणरूपादेः) - of māyic sense organs, physical form, etc.

एव - alone

ज्ञेयः - should be understood

तत्र - there (in these same śrutis)

दिव्यस्य (करणरूपादेः) रूपणात् - because of the description of Paramātman's divine sense organs and form.

The negation of Paramātman's sense organs and form heard in the śrutis[45] should be understood as the negation of māyic sense organs and physical form alone. This is because these same śrutis, indeed, also describe Paramātman's divine form.[46] (75)

45 'Śruti' literally means 'that which is heard'. The term refers to the Vedas, part of which includes the Upaniṣads. These texts are referred to as śrutis because Paramātman first revealed them to enlightened ṛṣis, who heard them and transmitted them to their disciples.

46 See, for instance, Bṛhadāraṇyakopaniṣad 1.4.1, Śvetāśvataropaniṣad 3.18, and Muṇḍakopaniṣad 3.1.3 (cited in Bhadreshdas, *Svāminārāyaṇa-siddhānta-sudhā*, 126).

तत्राऽपि मानवाकारः किशोरो द्विभुजः सदा।
चतुरष्टभुजत्वादि क्वाचित्कं स्वेच्छया कृतम्॥ ७६॥

tatrā'pi mānavākāraḥ kiśoro dvibhujaḥ sadā,
caturaṣṭabhujatvādi kvācitkaṃ svecchayā kṛtam.

पदच्छेदः - तत्र, अपि, मानवाकारः, किशोरः, द्विभुजः, सदा, चतुरष्टभुजत्वादि, क्वाचित्कम्, स्वेच्छया, कृतम्॥

अन्वयः

तत्र - there (in Akṣaradhāman)

अपि - indeed

(परमात्मा) - Paramātman

सदा - eternally

मानवाकारः - human form

किशोरः - youthful

द्विभुजः - possessing two arms

क्वाचित्कम् - at times

स्वेच्छया - by his own wish

चतुरष्टभुजत्वादि - the condition of possessing four arms, eight arms, etc.

कृतम् - is manifested

Indeed, Paramātman always has a human form in Akṣaradhāman; moreover, he is ever youthful and possesses a figure that has two arms. At his will, nonetheless, he sometimes takes upon a form possessing four arms, eight arms, or more. (76)

The author then explains that only worship offered with an understanding of Paramātman as possessing a divine form leads to liberation, while worship offered with an understanding of Paramātman as being formless is disdainful.

तस्माद्धरेः स्वरूपं तु साकारमेव सर्वदा।
इति भावनया नित्यं तदुपास्तिर्हि मोक्षदा॥ ७७॥

tasmāddhareeḥ svarūpaṃ tu sākārameva sarvadā,
iti bhāvanayā nityaṃ tadupāstirhi mokṣadā.

पदच्छेदः - तस्मात्, हरेः, स्वरूपम्, तु, साकारम्, एव, सर्वदा, इति, भावनया, नित्यम्, तदुपास्तिः, हि, मोक्षदा॥

अन्वयः

तस्माद् - therefore

हरेः - Paramātman's

स्वरूपम् - form

तु - indeed

सर्वदा - eternally

साकारम् - with form

एव - certainly

इति भावनया - with such understanding

नित्यम् - invariably

तदुपास्तिः - worship of Paramātman

हि - indeed

मोक्षदा - that which grants liberation

Therefore, worship of Paramātman with the understanding that Paramātman eternally possesses a form invariably grants liberation. (77)

निराकारादिभावाऽऽढ्या द्रोहनिग्रहबन्धकृत्।
साकारत्वे हरेः प्रीतिः शर्कराखण्डवद् बहुः ॥ ७८ ॥

nirākārādibhāvā''ḍhyā drohanigrahabandhakṛt,
sākāratve hareḥ prītiḥ śarkarākhaṇḍavad bahuḥ.

पदच्छेदः - निराकारादिभावाऽऽढ्या, द्रोहनिग्रहबन्धकृत्, साकारत्वे, हरेः, प्रीतिः, शर्कराखण्डवत्, बहुः ॥

अन्वयः

निराकारादिभावाऽऽढ्या (उपासना) - worship offered with the belief that Paramātman is formless

द्रोहनिग्रहबन्धकृत् - is a disgrace that brings upon Paramātman's displeasure and causes one to be bound [in māyā].

साकारत्वे - in the belief that he has a form

हरेः - God's

प्रीतिः - pleasure

शर्कराखण्डवद् - like sugar

बहुः - very much

(वर्तते) - is

Worshipping Paramātman as formless is a disgrace that brings upon Paramātman's displeasure and causes one to be bound in māyā. Paramātman's pleasure lies in the belief that he has a form. To him, this belief is as sweet as sugar. (78)

3.7 Pre-Eminence and Perennial Manifestation

The next two verses describe Paramātman's unmatched greatness and declare Swaminarayan himself as Paramātman.

स्वतः सर्वसमुत्कृष्टः सर्वत्र सर्वथा सदा।
गुणैश्वर्यादिभिः क्वाऽपि कोऽपि न तत्समो भवेत्॥ ७९ ॥

svataḥ sarvasamutkṛṣṭaḥ sarvatra sarvathā sadā,
guṇaiśvaryādibhiḥ kvā'pi ko'pi na tatsamo bhavet.

पदच्छेदः - स्वतः, सर्वसमुत्कृष्टः, सर्वत्र, सर्वथा, सदा, गुणैश्वर्यादिभिः, क्व, अपि, कः, अपि, न, तत्समः, भवेत्॥

अन्वयः

स्वतः - independently

सर्वत्र - everywhere

सर्वथा - in every way

सदा - always

सर्वसमुत्कृष्टः - far greater than all

(वर्तते) - is

गुणैश्वर्यादिभिः - by virtues and powers

तत्समः - one who is equal to him

क्वापि - anywhere

कोऽपि - anyone

न - not

भवेत् - is

He is independently far greater than all – everywhere, in every way, and always. In terms of virtues and powers, nowhere is there anyone equal to him. (79)

सोऽयं श्रीसहजानन्दः सर्वोपरि परात्परः।
स्वामिनारायणः साक्षाद् यस्मान्न विद्यते परः ॥ ८० ॥

so'yaṃ śrīsahajānandaḥ sarvopari parātparaḥ,
svāminārāyaṇaḥ sākṣād yasmānna vidyate paraḥ.

पदच्छेदः - सः, अयम्, श्रीसहजानन्दः, सर्वोपरि, परात्परः, स्वामिनारायणः, साक्षात्, यस्मात्, न, विद्यते, परः ॥

अन्वयः

सः - that

सर्वोपरि - supreme

परात्परः - transcends that which is superior

अयम् - this very

श्रीसहजानन्दः - Shri Sahajanand

स्वामिनारायणः - Swaminarayan

साक्षात् - himself

यस्मात् (च) - and from which

परः - above

न - does not

विद्यते - exist

This entity, which is supreme and transcends even that which is superior to all,[47] is this very Shri Sahajanand, or Swaminarayan himself. No entity is superior to him. (80)

47 See footnote 29 under verse 50.

The author now highlights the uniqueness of Bhagwan Swaminarayan's teaching that Paramātman is always present on earth through the Akṣarabrahman guru.

प्रत्यक्षोऽस्तीति सिद्धान्तं स्वामिनारायणो भुवि।
पूर्वमनुपदिष्टं च विशिष्टमाह शाश्वतम्॥ ८१॥

pratyakṣo'stīti siddhāntaṃ svāminārāyaṇo bhuvi,
pūrvamanupadiṣṭaṃ ca viśiṣṭamāha śāśvatam.

पदच्छेदः - प्रत्यक्षः, अस्ति, इति, सिद्धान्तम्, स्वामिनारायणः, भुवि, पूर्वम्, अनुपदिष्टम्, च, विशिष्टम्, आह, शाश्वतम्॥

अन्वयः

(परमात्मा) - Paramātman

भुवि - on earth

प्रत्यक्षः - manifest

अस्ति - is

इति - the aforementioned

पूर्वम् - before

अनुपदिष्टम् - unstated

विशिष्टम् - distinct

शाश्वतं च - and eternal

सिद्धान्तम् - principle

स्वामिनारायणः - Swaminarayan

आह - pronounced

Bhagwan Swaminarayan pronounced the previously unstated, distinct, and eternal principle that God is always manifest on earth. (81)

सेवितः सहजानन्दो भक्तैस्तत्कालिकैर्मुदा।
प्रत्यक्षं संप्रति ज्ञेयं गुरुरूपेण संस्थितम्॥ ८२॥

sevitaḥ sahajānando bhaktaistatkālikairmudā,
pratyakṣaṃ saṃprati jñeyaṃ gururūpeṇa saṃsthitam.

पदच्छेदः - सेवितः, सहजानन्दः, भक्तैः, तत्कालिकैः, मुदा, प्रत्यक्षम्, संप्रति, ज्ञेयम्, गुरुरूपेण, संस्थितम्॥

अन्वयः

तत्कालिकैः भक्तैः - by the devotees of his time

सहजानन्दः - Sahajanand (Swaminarayan)

मुदा - joyously

सेवितः - was served

सम्प्रति - currently

(सहजानन्दम्) - Sahajanand

गुरुरूपेण - through the [Akṣarabrahman] guru

प्रत्यक्षम् - manifest

संस्थितम् - residing

ज्ञेयम् - should be known

Swaminarayan was joyously served by the devotees of his time. Currently, he should be understood to be manifest through the Akṣarabrahman guru. (82)

The service and worship of the Akṣarabrahman guru are considered to be the service and worship of Paramātman himself, as the Akṣarabrahman guru embodies Paramātman. This principle is made clear through the following verse.

सम्यग् वासो यतस्तत्र ह्युद्भूतसर्वशक्तिकः ।
नारायणस्वरूपं तत् प्रत्यक्षमिति सेव्यते ॥ ८३ ॥

samyag vāso yatastatra hyudbhūtasarvaśaktikaḥ,
nārāyaṇasvarūpaṃ tat pratyakṣamiti sevyate.

पदच्छेदः - सम्यक्, वासः, यतः, तत्र, हि, उद्भूतसर्वशक्तिकः, नारायणस्वरूपम्, तत्, प्रत्यक्षम्, इति, सेव्यते ॥

अन्वयः

यतः - because

तत्र - there (within the Akṣarabrahman guru)

(परब्रह्मणः) - Parabrahman's

उद्भूतसर्वशक्तिकः - with all his sacred energy

सम्यक् - entirely

वासः - presence

हि - indeed

तत् - that (the Akṣarabrahman guru)

प्रत्यक्षम् - the manifest

नारायणस्वरूपम् - form of Nārāyaṇa

इति - thus

सेव्यते - is served

Parabrahman entirely resides within the Akṣarabrahman guru with all his sacred energy. Therefore, the guru is served as the manifest form of Nārāyaṇa. (83)

3.8 Inherent Divinity

To conclude, Paramātman's divinity and the fruit of realising this divinity are described.

दिव्यो दिव्याऽतिदिव्योऽयं स्वसङ्गाद् दिव्यताप्रदः ।
दिव्ये धाम्नि सदा दिव्यो दिव्य इह समागतः ॥ ८४ ॥

divyo divyā'tidivyo'yaṃ svasaṅgād divyatāpradaḥ,
divye dhāmni sadā divyo divya iha samāgataḥ.

पदच्छेदः - दिव्यः, दिव्याऽतिदिव्यः, अयम्, स्वसङ्गात्, दिव्यताप्रदः, दिव्ये, धाम्नि, सदा, दिव्यः, दिव्यः, इह, समागतः ॥

अन्वयः

अयम् - This entity (Paramātman)

दिव्यः - divine

दिव्याऽतिदिव्यः - supremely divine

स्वसङ्गात् - through his association

(मुमुक्षवे) - for the spiritual seeker

दिव्यताप्रदः - one who grants divinity

दिव्ये धाम्नि - in the divine abode

सदा - forever

दिव्यः - divine

इह समागतः - that which has come here

(अपि) - also

दिव्यः - divine

Paramātman is divine; indeed, he is supremely divine. He also grants divinity to those who associate with him. Indeed, he is eternally divine in his divine abode. His manifest form is also divine.[48] (84)

48 See footnote 40 under verse 69.

मानुषे दिव्यतां पश्यन् चिन्तयन् वर्णयन् लिखन्।
दिव्यानन्दं प्रभुञ्जीत कृपातो दिव्यतानिधेः॥ ८५॥

mānuṣe divyatāṃ paśyan cintayan varṇayan likhan,
divyānandaṃ prabhuñjīta kṛpāto divyatānidheḥ.

पदच्छेदः - मानुषे, दिव्यताम्, पश्यन्, चिन्तयन्, वर्णयन्, लिखन्, दिव्यानन्दम्, प्रभुञ्जीत, कृपातः, दिव्यतानिधेः॥

अन्वयः

मानुषे (स्वरूपे) - in Parabrahman's human form

दिव्यताम् - divinity

पश्यन् - one who sees

चिन्तयन् - one who reflects upon

वर्णयन् - one who speaks of

लिखन् (च) - and one who writes about

(भक्तः) - such a devotee

दिव्यतानिधेः कृपातः - through the grace of he who is an ocean of divinity

दिव्यानन्दम् - divine bliss

प्रभुञ्जीत - enjoys

The devotee who sees, reflects upon, speaks of, and writes about the divinity inherent in Paramātman's human form enjoys divine bliss through the grace of this very Paramātman, who is an ocean of divinity. (85)

एवं परब्रह्मस्वामिनारायणप्रबोधित-ब्रह्मस्वरूपगुणातीतगुरुपरम्परोपबृंहित-
ब्रह्मविद्यालक्षणाऽक्षरपुरुषोत्तमदर्शनप्रतिपादके
साधुभद्रेशदासविरचिते
स्वामिनारायणसिद्धान्तसुधाऽऽख्ये शास्त्रेऽस्मिन्
समाप्तं परब्रह्मधारा नाम
तृतीयं प्रकरणम् ॥

In this way ends the third chapter, known as the 'Parabrahma-dhārā', of Sadhu Bhadreshdas' *Svāminārāyaṇa-siddhānta-sudhā*, a text that substantiates the Akṣara-Puruṣottama Darśana, which is characterised as brahmavidyā, was taught by Parabrahman Swaminarayan, and has been fostered by the lineage of brahmasvarūpa, guṇātīta gurus.

Chapter 4

Pramāṇa-dhārā

4.1 Introduction

Many schools of Indian philosophy teach that liberation is secured through experiential knowledge of the self, the world, and the Divine. To this end, the means of attaining knowledge becomes just as important as knowledge itself, as knowledge must be valid in order to liberate. Much of Indian philosophy thus earnestly reflects on various means of knowledge. It often refers to these means as 'pramāṇas' and divides them into groups such as pratyakṣa (perception), anumāna (inference), upamāna (analogy), śabda (verbal testimony), arthāpatti (postulation) and anupalabdhi (non-cognition).

The Akṣara-Puruṣottama Darśana authenticates all means of knowledge, arguing that the knowledge event supersedes the means of attaining knowledge. However, it privileges śabda over the other pramāṇas, arguing that it is the only means through which one can understand that which is divine.

The author begins this chapter by revering the entities of Akṣara and Puruṣottama as the grounds of valid knowledge and the cause of the pramāṇas. He also hails Pramukh Swami Maharaj as the manifest form validation. He then defines knowledge and its relation to the ātman. Thereafter, he elaborates on two pramāṇas – perception and inference. He describes two types of each pramāṇa and explains how valid knowledge is obtained through these pramāṇas.

The chapter then discusses 'śabda', or verbal testimony. It first defines what the term 'śabda' encompasses. In particular, it expresses that Parabrahman Swaminarayan's and the Akṣarabrahman guru's words are preeminently authoritative, as are the Vedas. With this in mind, it describes as supremely authoritative the following texts: Bhagwan Swaminarayan's teachings, compiled as the Vacanāmṛta; Akṣarabrahman Gunatitanand Swami's discourses, compiled as the Svāmīnī Vāto; and the works documenting the lives of Parabrahman Swaminarayan and the Akṣarabrahman gurus. It describes these texts as the sampradāya's prasthānatrayī or the fellowship's three foundational texts.

Upon arguing for the significance of śāstras, however, the text places the guru's words in a higher position than the śāstras. It argues that śāstras alone cannot lead to wisdom, faith, or bliss. Instead, it posits that the śāstras should be learned and imbibed through association with the Akṣarabrahman guru.

4.2 Benediction

The author begins the 'Pramāṇa-dhārā' with three verses that offer homage to Swaminarayan as the cause of 1) the pramāṇas, 2) the valid knowledge that arises from the pramāṇas, and 3) the objects of such valid knowledge. He also bows to his guru, who he describes as the manifest form of validation.

यत्संकल्पाऽनुगं वस्तुभूतिस्थित्यादि सर्वदा।
यत्संकल्पाऽनुगो वस्तुस्वरूपधर्मनिश्चयः ॥ ८६ ॥

yatsaṃkalpā'nugaṃ vastubhūtisthityādi sarvadā,
yatsaṃkalpā'nugo vastusvarūpadharmaniścayaḥ.

पदच्छेदः - यत्संकल्पाऽनुगम्, वस्तुभूतिस्थित्यादि, सर्वदा, यत्संकल्पऽनुगः वस्तुस्वरूपधर्मनिश्चयः ॥

अन्वयः

यत्सङ्कल्पानुगम् - according to whose will

सर्वदा - eternally

वस्तु-भूति-स्थिति-आदि - the cause, sustenance, and destruction of objects

(भवति) - occurs

यत्सङ्कल्पानुगः - according to whose will

वस्तु-स्वरूप-धर्म-निश्चयः - the form and attributes of all objects are determined

According to whose will the cause, sustenance, and destruction of objects eternally occurs; according to whose will the form and attributes of objects are determined; (86)

यश्च प्रामाण्यनिर्णेता सर्वप्रामाण्यकारणम्।
सर्वप्रामाण्यधीहेतुः सर्वप्रमाप्रदः प्रमी॥ ८७॥

yaśca prāmāṇyanirṇetā sarvaprāmāṇyakāraṇam,
sarvaprāmāṇyadhīhetuḥ sarvapramāpradaḥ pramī.

पदच्छेदः - यः, च, प्रामाण्यनिर्णेता, सर्वप्रामाण्यकारणम्, सर्वप्रामाण्यधीहेतुः, सर्वप्रमाप्रदः, प्रमी॥

अन्वयः

यः - he who

प्रामाण्यनिर्णेता - the establisher of validity

सर्वप्रामाण्यकारणम् - the source of the means of knowledge

सर्वप्रामाण्यधीहेतुः - that which begets knowledge of validity

सर्वप्रमाप्रदः - that which begets valid knowledge

प्रमी - the knower

च - and

(भवति) - is

He who is the establisher and source of validity; he who begets both the knowledge of validity and valid knowledge; and he who is the knower; (87)

स्वामिनारायणं वन्दे ह्यक्षरपुरुषोत्तमम्।
प्रमाणपुरुषं वन्दे प्रमुखं तं गुरुं हरिम्॥ ८८॥

svāminārāyaṇaṃ vande hyakṣarapuruṣottamam,
pramāṇapuruṣaṃ vande pramukhaṃ taṃ guruṃ harim.

पदच्छेदः - स्वामिनारायणम्, वन्दे, हि, अक्षरपुरुषोत्तमम्, प्रमाणपुरुषम्, वन्दे, प्रमुखम्, तम्, गुरुम्, हरिम्॥

अन्वयः

तम् - that

स्वामिनारायणम् - Swaminarayan

हि - indeed

अक्षरपुरुषोत्तमम् - Akṣara-Puruṣottama

वन्दे - I bow to

(तथा) - also

प्रमाणपुरुषम् - he who is the form of validation

गुरुं हरिम् - to guru-hari (God in the form of the guru)

प्रमुखम् - Pramukh (Swami Maharaj)

वन्दे - I bow

I bow to this entity, Swaminarayan, also known as Akṣara-Puruṣottama. I also bow to guru-hari Pramukh Swami Maharaj, the manifest form of validation. (88)

4.3 Knowledge

ज्ञानं प्रमात्मकं ज्ञेयं यथाऽवस्थितवस्तुनः ।
यथा शुक्तावियं शुक्ती रजते रजतं तथा ॥ ८९ ॥

jñānaṃ pramātmakaṃ jñeyaṃ yathā'vasthitavastunaḥ,
yathā śuktāviyaṃ śuktī rajate rajataṃ tathā.

पदच्छेदः - ज्ञानम्, प्रमात्मकम्, ज्ञेयम्, यथाऽवस्थितवस्तुनः, यथा, शुक्तौ, इयम्, शुक्तिः, रजते, रजतम्, तथा ॥

अन्वयः

यथाऽवस्थितवस्तुनः - an object as it stands existentially

प्रमात्मकम् - that which is characterised by validity

ज्ञानम् - knowledge

ज्ञेयम् - should be known as

यथा - just as

शुक्तौ - in a shell

इयम् - this

शुक्तिः - a shell

(अस्ति) - is

रजते (च) - and in silver

(इदम्) - this

रजतम् - silver

(अस्ति) - is

तथा - in this way

Knowledge should be known as the valid understanding of an object as it is. For instance, in the case of a shell, knowledge is the idea of the object being a shell; in the case of silver, it is the idea of the object being silver. (89)

अकार्त्स्न्यं वैपरीत्यं च तथैव संशयादिकम् ।
अपाकृत्य विबोधे स्यात् प्रमाणमुपकारकम् ॥ ९० ॥

akārtsnyaṃ vaiparītyaṃ ca tathaiva saṃśayādikam,
apākṛtya vibodhane pramāṇamupakārakam.

पदच्छेदः - अकार्त्स्न्यम्, वैपरीत्यम्, च, तथा, एव, संशयादिकम्, अपाकृत्य, विबोधे, स्यात्, प्रमाणम् उपकारकम् ॥

अन्वयः

अकार्त्स्न्यम् - incompleteness

वैपरीत्यम् च - and delusion

संशयादिकम् तथा - doubt and other factors

एव - indeed

अपाकृत्य - having done away with

विबोधे - in the act of knowing

प्रमाणम् - an instrument of knowledge

उपकारकम् - beneficial.

स्यात् - is

Indeed, when incompleteness, delusion, doubt, and other mitigating factors are cast aside, instruments of knowledge are useful in the pursuit of wisdom. (90)

आत्मा ज्ञानाऽविनाभावी ज्ञानमात्रविहीनताम् ।
न भजते यतो ह्ययमनादिसंसृतिं गतः ॥९१॥

ātmā jñānā'vinābhāvī jñānamātravihīnatām,
na bhajate yato hyayamanādisaṃsṛtiṃ gataḥ.

पदच्छेदः - आत्मा, ज्ञानाऽविनाभावी, ज्ञानमात्रविहीनताम्, न, भजते, यतः, हि, अयम्, अनादिसंसृतिम्, गतः ॥

अन्वयः

ज्ञानाऽविनाभावी - that which never does not coexist with knowledge

आत्मा - the ātman

ज्ञानमात्रविहीनताम् - a state that is devoid of all types of knowledge

न - does not

भजते - experience

यतः - because

अयम् - this [ātman]

हि - indeed

अनादिसंसृतिम् - beginning-less saṃsāra

गतः - has attained

The ātman is never without knowledge; that is, it never experiences a state wherein it is devoid of all types of knowledge. This is because it has been eternally engulfed in saṃsāra. (91)

4.4 Perception

Pratyakṣa is one of the means of attaining knowledge. The knowledge attained from pratyakṣa pramāna is called pratyakṣa jñāna. This verse describes the two types of pratyakṣa jñāna.

प्रत्यक्षं द्विविधं ज्ञेयं लौकिकं च ह्यलौकिकम् ।
आद्यमिन्द्रियसापेक्षं बद्धजीवेश्वरात्मनाम् ॥ ९२ ॥

pratyakṣaṃ dvividhaṃ jñeyaṃ laukikaṃ ca hyalaukikam,
ādyamindriyasāpekṣaṃ baddhajīveśvarātmanām.

पदच्छेदः - प्रत्यक्षम्, द्विविधम्, ज्ञेयम्, लौकिकम्, च, हि, अलौकिकम्, आद्यम्, इन्द्रियसापेक्षम्, बद्धजीवेश्वरात्मनाम् ॥

अन्वयः

द्विविधम् - of two types

प्रत्यक्षम् - knowledge that arises from perception

ज्ञेयम् - should be understood

हि - certainly

लौकिकम् - that which is sensory.

अलौकिकम् - that which is beyond the senses

च - and

आद्यम् - the first

बद्धजीवेश्वरात्मनाम् - of bound jīvas and īśvaras

इन्द्रियसापेक्षम् - is dependent upon the senses

Knowledge that arises from perception should be understood to be of two types: that which is ascertained through the senses and that which is beyond the senses. Of these, the prior, which is dependent upon the senses, is that of bound jīvas and īśvaras. (92)

In the Svāminārāyaṇa-siddhānta-sudhā, the author here before also describes knowledge that is beyond the senses. Afterwards, he proceeds to further elaborate on knowledge that is dependent on the senses.

सापेक्षं द्विविधं ज्ञेयं बाह्यमाभ्यन्तरं तथा ।
समनश्चक्षुरादीनां बाह्यं विषयसंगतः ॥९३॥

sāpekṣaṃ dvividhaṃ jñeyaṃ bāhyamābhyantaraṃ tathā,
samanaścakṣurādīnāṃ bāhyaṃ viṣayasaṃgataḥ.

पदच्छेदः - सापेक्षम्, द्विविधम्, ज्ञेयम्, बाह्यम्, आभ्यन्तरम्, तथा, समनश्चक्षुरादीनाम्, बाह्यम्, विषयसंगतः ॥

अन्वयः

द्विविधम् - of two types

सापेक्षम् - dependence (on the senses)

ज्ञेयम् - should be understood

बाह्यम् - external

आभ्यन्तरं तथा - and internal

विषयसंगतः - due to contact with the objects of the senses

बाह्यम् - external [dependence]

समनश्चक्षुरादीनाम् - that which relies on the eyes and other gross senses, which must necessarily be accompanied by the mind

(सापेक्षम्) - reliance

Dependence on the senses should be known to be of two types: external and internal. Of these, the first occurs when the eyes and other physical senses, accompanied by the mind, connect with external objects. (93)

बाह्येन्द्रियऽनपेक्षं यदन्तः समृत्यादि मानसम् ।
षड्विधकरणाऽपेक्षं तदपि षड्विधं भवेत् ॥९४॥

bāhyendriya'napekṣaṃ yadantaḥ samṛtyādi mānasam,
ṣaḍvidhakaraṇā'pekṣaṃ tadapi ṣaḍvidhaṃ bhavet.

पदच्छेदः - बाह्येन्द्रियऽनपेक्षम्, यद्, अन्तः, स्मृत्यादि, मानसम्, षड्विधकरणाऽपेक्षम्, तद्, अपि, षड्विधम्, भवेत् ॥

अन्वयः

बाह्येन्द्रियऽनपेक्षम् - that which is not dependent on external senses

स्मृत्यादि - recollection and other

मानसम् - cognitive

यद् - that which

अन्तः - internal

(प्रत्यक्षम्) - perception

षड्विधकरणाऽपेक्षम् - is dependent upon the six senses

तद् - that

अपि - also

षड्विधम् - of six types

भवेत् - is

Perception that does not rely on external senses, such as recollection etc., is internal perception. The six senses (including the mind) give rise to perception; therefore, perception is also of six types. (94)

आत्माऽन्तःकरणाऽऽढ्यं स्यात् प्रमाणं चक्षुरादिकम् ।
विषयग्राहकाणि स्युरिन्द्रियाणि स्ववृत्तिभिः ॥ ९५ ॥

ātmā'ntaḥkaraṇā''ḍhyaṃ syāt pramāṇaṃ cakṣurādikam,
viṣayagrāhakāṇi syurindriyāṇi svavṛttibhiḥ.

<u>पदच्छेदः</u> - आत्माऽन्तःकरणाऽऽढ्यम्, स्यात्, प्रमाणम्, चक्षुरादिकम् । विषयग्राहकाणि, स्युः, इन्द्रियाणि, स्ववृत्तिभिः ॥

<u>अन्वयः -</u>

चक्षुरादिकम् - the eyes and other gross senses

आत्माऽन्तःकरणाऽऽढ्यम् - that which is enhanced by the ātman and the inner faculties, such as the mind and intellect

(एव) - only

प्रमाणम् - instrument of knowledge

स्यात् - is

(तानि) इन्द्रियाणि - these gross senses

(च) - moreover

स्ववृत्तिभिः - through their vṛttis (idiosyncratic emanations)

विषयग्राहकाणि - grasp their objects

स्युः - are

The eyes and other gross senses are instruments of knowledge only when empowered by the ātman and the inner faculties. These gross senses grasp their objects through their vṛttis (idiosyncratic emanations). (95)

4.5 Inference

अनु हेतुमितिं नित्यं साध्यस्य जायते मितिः।
तस्मादनुमितिः प्रोक्ता प्रमाणस्थाऽनुमानजा ॥ ९६ ॥

anu hetumitiṃ nityaṃ sādhyasya jāyate mitiḥ,
tasmādanumitiḥ proktā pramāṇasthā'numānajā.

पदच्छेदः - अनु, हेतुमितिम्, नित्यम्, साध्यस्य, जायते, मितिः, तस्मात्, अनुमितिः, प्रोक्ता, प्रमाणस्थाऽनुमानजा ॥

अन्वयः

नित्यम् - always

हेतुमितिम् - knowledge of the reason for inference

अनु - after

साध्यस्य - of that which is inferred

मितिः - knowledge

जायते - is created

तस्मात् - therefore

प्रमाणस्था - that which stands amidst the means of obtaining valid knowledge

अनुमानजा - that which is born from inference

अनुमितिः - inferred knowledge

प्रोक्ता - is described as

It is always the case that knowledge of that which is inferred arises only after knowledge of the reason for inference arises. Therefore, inferred knowledge is described as being born from inference. (96)

अनुमानं द्विधं प्रोक्तं स्वार्थपरार्थभेदयोः ।
स्वार्थं स्वाऽनुमितेर्हेतुः पराऽनुमितिकृत्परम् ॥ ९७ ॥

anumānaṃ dvidhaṃ proktaṃ svārthaparārthabhedayoḥ,
svārthaṃ svā'numiterhetuḥ parā'numitikṛtparam.

पदच्छेदः - अनुमानम्, द्विधम्, प्रोक्तम्, स्वार्थपरार्थभेदयोः, स्वार्थम्, स्वाऽनुमितेः, हेतुः, पराऽनुमितिकृत्, परम् ॥

अन्वयः

स्वार्थपरार्थभेदयोः - due to the distinction between the svārtha and parārtha

द्विधम् - of two types

अनुमानम् - inference

प्रोक्तम् - is described

स्वार्थम् - the svārtha

स्वाऽनुमितेः - of one's own inferential knowledge

हेतुः - the cause

परम् - the latter

परानुमितिकृत् - that which engenders knowledge for others.

Inference is described as being of two types: svārtha and parārtha. The svārtha engenders knowledge for oneself; the latter engenders knowledge for others. (97)

हेतुवद्धि यदाभासो हेतवो दूषिता मताः ।
हेत्वाभासास्ततो ज्ञेया व्याप्त्यनुमितिरोधकाः ॥ ९८ ॥

hetuvaddhi yadābhāso hetavo dūṣitā matāḥ,
hetvābhāsāstato jñeyā vyāptyanumitirodhakāḥ.

पदच्छेदः - हेतुवद्, हि, यद्, आभासः, हेतवः, दूषिताः, मताः, हेत्वाभासाः, ततः, ज्ञेयाः, व्याप्त्यनुमितिरोधकाः ॥

अन्वयः

हेतुवद् हि यदाभासः - that which is misconceived as a cause

(ते) - those

दूषिताः - erroneous

हेतवः - causes

मताः - are known as

ततः - therefore

हेत्वाभासाः - that which is a semblance of a cause of inference

ज्ञेयाः - should be known as

(ये) - that which

व्याप्त्यनुमितिरोधकाः - that which hinders knowledge of invariable concomitance and knowledge arising from inference

Those which are misconceived as a cause are erroneous causes. These erroneous causes hinder knowledge of invariable concomitance and knowledge arising from inference. Therefore, they should be known as 'hetvābhāsāḥ' (98)

हेतुरुपमितेर्यः स्यादुपमानं तदुच्यते ।
शास्त्रोपयोगबाहुल्यात् प्रामाण्यं न जहाति तत् ॥ ९९ ॥

heturupamiteryaḥ syādupamānaṃ taducyate,
śāstropayogabāhulyāt prāmāṇyaṃ na jahāti tat.

पदच्छेदः - हेतुः, उपमितेः, यः, स्यात्, उपमानम्, तद्, उच्यते, शास्त्रोपयोगबाहुल्यात्, प्रामाण्यम्, न, जहाति, तत् ॥

अन्वयः

उपमितेः - of knowledge arising from resemblance

यः - that which

हेतुः - cause

स्यात् - is

तद् - that

उपमानम् - comparison

उच्यते - is said to be

(उपमानस्य) - comparison's

शास्त्रोपयोगबाहुल्यात् - due to its prevalent use in the śāstras

(तत्) - it

प्रामाण्यम् - validity

न - does not

जहाति - renounce

Comparison is said to be the cause of the knowledge that arises from resemblance. It is a valid means to knowledge due to its prevalent use in the śāstras. (99)

4.6 Verbal Testimony

शब्दो यो हि यथार्थः स्यात् प्रामाण्यं भजते सदा ।
अन्यथा नैव प्रामाण्यं दुष्टशब्दादनर्थधीः ॥१००॥

śabdo yo hi yathārthaḥ syāt prāmāṇyaṃ bhajate sadā,
anyathā naiva prāmāṇyaṃ duṣṭaśabdādanarthadhīḥ.

<u>पदच्छेदः</u> - शब्दः, यः, हि, यथार्थः, स्यात्, प्रामाण्यम्, भजते, सदा, अन्यथा, न, एव, प्रामाण्यम्, दुष्टशब्दात्, अनर्थधीः ॥

<u>अन्वयः</u>

यः - that which

यथार्थः - precise

शब्दः - verbal testimony

स्यात् - is

प्रामाण्यम् - authenticity as a means to valid knowledge

हि - indeed

भजते - enjoys

सदा - always

अन्यथा - otherwise

दुष्टशब्दात् - from unprecise verbal testimony

अनर्थधीः - inaccurate knowledge

(भवति) - arises

(तस्य दुष्टशब्दस्य) - of this unprecise verbal testimony

न - not

एव - certainly

प्रामाण्यम् - authenticity as a means to valid knowledge

Precise verbal testimony indeed enjoys authenticity as a means to valid knowledge at all times. On the other hand, unprecise verbal testimony, which gives rise to inaccurate knowledge, certainly does not carry authenticity as a means to valid knowledge. (100)

हरेर्गुरोश्च यः शब्दः प्रमाणं निखिलो मतः ।
तदुपदिष्टं सच्छास्त्रं प्रमाणं तत्कृताऽर्थकम् ॥ १०१ ॥

harergurośca yaḥ śabdaḥ pramāṇaṃ nikhilo mataḥ,
tadupadiṣṭaṃ sacchāstraṃ pramāṇaṃ tatkṛtā'rthakam.

पदच्छेदः - हरेः, गुरोः, च, यः, शब्दः, प्रमाणम्, निखिलः, मतः, तदुपदिष्टम्, सच्छास्त्रम्, प्रमाणम्, तत्कृताऽर्थकम् ॥

अन्वयः

हरेः - of Parabrahman

गुरोः - of the Akṣarabrahman guru

च - and

यः - that which

निखिलः - the entirety of

शब्दः - word

प्रमाणम् - authoritative

मतः - is understood

तदुपदिष्टम् - taught by them

तत्कृताऽर्थकम् - according to meaning offered by them

सच्छास्त्रम् - śāstra

प्रमाणम् - authoritative

(अस्ति) - is

Parabrahman's and the Akṣarabrahman guru's words, in their entirety, are understood to be authoritative. Śāstra that incorporates Parabrahman's and Akṣarabrahman's teachings and is in accordance with their explanations is also authoritative. (101)

संहिताब्राह्मणात्मा यस्तथोपनिषदात्मकः ।
आरण्यकस्वरूपश्च वेदः प्रामाण्यभाग् भवेत् ॥ १०२ ॥

saṃhitābrāhmaṇātmā yastathopaniṣadātmakaḥ,
āraṇyakasvarūpaśca vedaḥ prāmāṇyabhāg bhavet.

पदच्छेदः - संहिताब्राह्मणात्मा, यः, तथा, उपनिषदात्मकः, आरण्यकस्वरूपः, च, वेदः, प्रमाण्यभाग्, भवेत् ॥

अन्वयः

यः - that which

संहिताब्राह्मणात्मा - in the form of the Saṃhitās and the Brāhmaṇas

उपनिषदात्मकः - in the form of the Upaniṣads

तथा - and

आरण्यकस्वरूपः - in the form of the Āraṇyakas

च - and

वेदः - the Veda

प्रामाण्यभाग् - the enjoyer of authoritativeness

भवेत् - is

The Veda, which appears in the form of the Saṃhitās, Brāhmaṇas, Upaniṣads, and Āraṇyakas, is understood to be authoritative. (102)

शिक्षादीनां तदङ्गानां वेदरक्षा प्रयोजनम् ।
वेदपीडा भवेन्नूनं वैपरीत्यात् पदार्थयोः ॥ १०३ ॥

śikṣādīnāṃ tadaṅgānāṃ vedarakṣā prayojanam,
vedapīḍā bhavennūnaṃ vaiparītyāt padārthayoḥ.

पदच्छेदः - शिक्षादीनाम्, तदङ्गानाम्, वेदरक्षा, प्रयोजनम्, वेदपीडा भवेत्, नूनम्, वैपरीत्यात्, पदार्थयोः ॥

अन्वयः

तदङ्गानाम् - its (the Veda's) auxiliary texts

शिक्षादीनाम् - the Śikṣā and others

प्रयोजनम् - purpose

वेदरक्षा - safeguarding the Veda

नूनम् - indeed

पदार्थयोः - words and their meanings

वैपरीत्यात् - due to inconsistency

वेदपीडा - harm to the Veda

भवेत् - occurs

The Śikṣā and other auxiliary texts safeguard the Veda. Indeed, inconsistency between words and their meanings brings harm to the Veda [by giving rise to false interpretation]. (103)

इतिहासपुराणाभ्यां तस्मात् तदुपबृंहणम् ।
सदाचारेण शिष्टानां वेदार्थोज्जीवनं भुवि ॥ १०४॥

itihāsapurāṇābhyāṃ tasmāt tadupabṛṃhaṇam,
sadācāreṇa śiṣṭānāṃ vedārthojjīvanaṃ bhuvi.

<u>पदच्छेदः</u> - इतिहासपुराणाभ्याम्, तस्मात्, तदुपबृंहणम्, सदाचारेण, शिष्टानाम्, वेदार्थोज्जीवनम्, भुवि ॥

<u>अन्वयः</u>

तस्मात् - therefore

इतिहासपुराणाभ्याम् - through the itihāsas and purāṇas

तदुपबृंहणम् - its elucidation

शिष्टानाम् - of those who are wise

(च) - moreover

सदाचारेण - through virtuous conduct

भुवि - in the world

वेदार्थोज्जीवनम् - the Veda's values thrive

Therefore, the Veda is elucidated through the itihāsas and purāṇas. Moreover, the Veda's values continue to thrive in the world through the virtuous conduct of those who are wise. (104)

साक्षाद्वेदो भवेद् वाक्यं स्वामिनारायणप्रभोः।
गुरुश्च पञ्चमो वेदस्तच्छब्दश्रेष्ठता ततः॥ १०५॥

itihāsapurāṇābhyāṃ tasmāt tadupabṛṃhaṇam,
sadācāreṇa śiṣṭānāṃ vedārthojjīvanaṃ bhuvi.

पदच्छेदः - साक्षात्, वेदः, भवेत्, वाक्यम्, स्वामिनारायणप्रभोः, गुरुः, च, पञ्चमः, वेदः, तच्छब्दश्रेष्ठता, ततः॥

अन्वयः

स्वामिनारायणप्रभोः - Bhagwan Swaminarayan's

वाक्यम् - word

साक्षाद् - itself

वेदः - the Veda

भवेत् - is

गुरुः च - and the Akṣarabrahman guru

पञ्चमो वेदः - the fifth Veda

ततः - therefore

तच्छब्दश्रेष्ठता - their words carry preeminence

Bhagwan Swaminarayan's word is equivalent to the Veda itself. The Akṣarabrahman guru, moreover, is the fifth Veda. Therefore, Swaminarayan's and the Akṣarabrahman guru's words are preeminent.[49] (105)

49 The Vedic corpus consists of four parts – the Ṛg, Sama, Yajur, and Atharva Vedas. In this verse, though, the author equates Swaminarayan's and the Akṣarabrahman guru's words with the Vedas in order to explain their supreme authority. Indeed, just as the Vedas are considered direct revelation, Parabrahman Swaminarayan's words and the Akṣarabrahman guru's words also entail direct revelation and are, thus, just as authoritative as the Vedas.

The author now enumerates the texts in which Swaminarayan's and the Akṣarabrahman guru's words appear.

वचनामृतशास्त्रं हि वार्ताश्च स्वामिनः शुभाः ।
गुरुचरित्रग्रन्थाश्च प्रस्थानत्रयमुच्यते ॥ १०६ ॥

vacanāmṛtaśāstraṃ hi vārtāśca svāminaḥ śubhāḥ,
gurucaritragranthāśca prasthānatrayamucyate.

पदच्छेदः - वचनामृतशास्त्रम्, हि, वार्ताः, च, स्वामिनः, शुभाः, गुरुचरित्रग्रन्थाः च, प्रस्थानत्रयम्, उच्यते ॥

अन्वयः

वचनामृतशास्त्रम् - The Vacanāmṛta

स्वामिनः - [Gunatitanand] Swami's

शुभाः - auspicious

वार्ताः - talks

च - and

हि - certainly

गुरुचरित्रग्रन्थाः - the texts documenting the lives of the gurus

च - and

(साम्प्रदायिकम्) - of the sampradāya

प्रस्थानत्रयम् - the prasthānatrayī (the three foundational texts)

उच्यते - known as

The Vacanāmṛta, Gunatitanand Swami's auspicious talks (the Svāmīnī Vāto), and the texts documenting the lives of the Akṣarabrahman gurus are known as the prasthānatrayī (the three foundational texts) of the sampradāya. (106)

सिद्धान्ताऽनुगमन्यत्तु सर्वथा साम्प्रदायिकम्।
गुरुप्रमाणितं ह्येव प्रामाण्यपदवीं भजेत्॥ १०७॥

siddhāntā'nugamanyattu sarvathā sāmpradāyikam,
gurupramāṇitaṃ hyeva prāmāṇyapadavīṃ bhajet.

पदच्छेदः - सिद्धान्ताऽनुगमम्, अन्यत्, तु, सर्वथा, साम्प्रदायिकम्, गुरुप्रमाणितम्, हि, एव, प्रामाण्यपदवीम्, भजेत्॥

अन्वयः

अन्यत् साम्प्रदायिकम् (शास्त्रम्) - other śāstras of the sampradāya

तु - on the other hand

सर्वथा - in every way

सिद्धान्ताऽनुगम् - according to the sampradāya's principles

गुरुप्रमाणितम् (च) - and corroborated by the guru

हि - indeed

(तत्) एव (शास्त्रम्) - that śāstra alone

प्रामाण्यपदवीम् - authority

भजेत् - enjoys

Other sāmpradāyika texts that endorse the sampradāya's principles in every way and are corroborated by the guru alone indeed, are authoritative. (107)

प्रत्यक्षादिप्रमाणेषु शब्दस्तु प्रमुखो भवेत् ।
यस्मादलौकिकाऽर्थेषु शब्दाऽन्यप्रसरो न हि ॥ १०८ ॥

pratyakṣādipramāṇeṣu śabdastu pramukho bhavet,
yasmādalaukikā'rtheṣu śabdā'nyaprasaro na hi.

पदच्छेदः - प्रत्यक्षादिप्रमाणेषु, शब्दः, तु, प्रमुखः, भवेत्, यस्मात्, अलौकिकाऽर्थेषु, शब्दाऽन्यप्रसरः, न, हि ॥

अन्वयः

प्रत्यक्षादिप्रमाणेषु - amongst perception and the other methods of obtaining knowledge

तु - certainly

शब्दः - verbal testimony

प्रमुखः - chief

भवेत् - is

यस्मात् - because

अलौकिकाऽर्थेषु - in other-worldly objects

न (भवति) - does not occur

हि - indeed

शब्दाऽन्यप्रसरः - the reach of methods other than verbal testimony

Amongst perception and the other methods of obtaining valid knowledge, verbal testimony is certainly the most authoritative. This is because, undoubtedly, methods of knowledge other than verbal testimony cannot reach those objects that are not of this world. (108)

केवलमनुमानं तु परात्मसाधकं न हि ।
व्यभिचारादिदोषत्वं कार्यत्वादेर्न वार्यते ॥ १०९ ॥

kevalamanumānaṃ tu parātmasādhakaṃ na hi,
vyabhicārādidoṣatvaṃ kāryatvāderna vāryate.

पदच्छेदः - केवलम्, अनुमानम्, तु, परात्मसाधकम्, न, हि, व्यभिचारादिदोषत्वम्, कार्यत्वादेः, न, वार्यते ॥

अन्वयः

केवलम् - alone

अनुमानम् - inference

तु - certainly

न - not

हि - indeed

परत्मसाधकम् - that which proves [the existence of] Paramātman

कार्यत्वादेः (हेतोः) - based on the reason of there being an effect [in the form of creation]

(कर्तृत्वस्य अनुमाने) - the inference that there is a cause [in the form of Paramātman]

व्यभिचारादिदोषत्वम् - fallaciousness and other types of [logical] error

न - not

वार्यते - resolved

Inference alone certainly cannot prove Paramātman's existence. Verily, fallaciousness and other types of logical error are not resolved when it is reasoned that the existence of an effect (creation) necessitates the existence of a cause (Paramātman). (109)

अतः शास्त्राऽऽश्रयो श्रेयान् अनुमानादलौकिके ।
जगत्कर्तृत्वबोधाय ह्यक्षरे पुरुषोत्तमे ॥ ११० ॥

ataḥ śāstrā''śrayo śreyān anumānādalaukike,
jagatkartṛtvabodhāya hyakṣare puruṣottame.

पदच्छेदः - अतः, शास्त्राऽऽश्रयः, श्रेयान्, अनुमानादलौकिके, जगत्कर्तृत्वबोधाय, हि, अक्षरे, पुरुषोत्तमे ॥

अन्वयः

अतः - therefore

अलौकिके - in that which is not of this world

अक्षरे - in Akṣara

पुरुषोत्तमे (च) - and in Puruṣottama

जगत्कर्तृत्वबोधाय - for knowledge of the causality of creation

अनुमानादिलौकिके (प्रमाणे) - in comparison to inference and other, ordinary means of obtaining knowledge

हि - certainly

श्रेयान् - superior

शास्त्राऽऽश्रयः - reliance on śāstra.

Therefore, for knowledge of Akṣara and Puruṣottama's cosmogonic causality, reliance on śāstra is superior to dependence on inference and other, ordinary means of knowledge acquisition. (110)

शास्त्रशब्दोऽपि नो सेव्यो गुरोराश्रयणं विना।
गुरुमुखाच्छ्रुतं शास्त्रं सदर्थांस्तु प्रकाशयेत्॥ १११॥

ataḥ śāstrā''śrayo śreyān anumānādalaukike,
jagatkartṛtvabodhāya hyakṣare puruṣottame.

<u>पदच्छेद:</u> - शास्त्रशब्द:, अपि, नो, सेव्य:, गुरो:, आश्रयणम्, विना, गुरुमुखात्, श्रुतम्, शास्त्रम्, सदर्थान्, तु, प्रकाशयेत्॥

<u>अन्वय:</u>

गुरो: - the guru's

आश्रयणम् - refuge

विना - without

शास्त्रशब्द: - the śāstra's words

अपि - however

नो सेव्य: - should not be resorted to

(यदा) - when

शास्त्रम् - śāstra

गुरुमुखात् - from the guru's mouth

श्रुतम् - is heard

(तदा एव) - only then

सदर्थान् - truth

तु - indeed

प्रकाशयेत् - is illumined

However, even the words of the śāstras must not be resorted to without having taken the brahmasvarūpa guru's refuge. Truth, indeed, is only illumined when śāstra is heard from the guru. (111)

गुरुहरिबलं श्रेष्ठं शास्त्रवचोबलादपि।
शास्त्रात्तु केवलात् क्वापि न ज्ञानं निश्चयः सुखम्॥ ११२॥

guruharibalaṃ śreṣṭhaṃ śāstravacobalādapi,
śāstrāttu kevalāt kvāpi na jñānaṃ niścayaḥ sukham.

पदच्छेदः - गुरुहरिबलम्, श्रेष्ठम्, शास्त्रवचोबलात्, अपि, शास्त्रात्, तु, केवलात्, क्व, अपि, न, ज्ञानम्, निश्चयः, सुखम्॥

अन्वयः

शास्त्रवचोबलाद् अपि - even than the strength of the śāstras' words

गुरुहरिबलम् - the guru-hari's strength

श्रेष्ठम् - is greater

केवलात् शास्त्रात् - only from the śāstras

तु - certainly

क्वापि - absolutely anywhere

ज्ञानम् - wisdom

निश्चयः - faith

सुखम् (वा) - or bliss

न (भवति) - does not occur

The guru-hari's strength is greater than the strength of the śāstras' words, as the śāstras' words alone can certainly never lead to wisdom, faith, or bliss. (112)

4.7 The Preeminence of the Knowledge Event

प्रत्यनीकं भवेद् यद्धि प्रमायां करणं न हि ।
प्रमित्यनुगुणत्वे तु न तत्संख्यादुराग्रहः ॥ ११३ ॥

pratyanīkaṃ bhaved yaddhi pramāyāṃ karaṇaṃ na hi,
pramityanuguṇatve tu na tatsaṃkhyādurāgrahaḥ.

पदच्छेदः - प्रत्यनीकम्, भवेत्, यद्, हि, प्रमायाम्, करणम्, न, हि, प्रमित्यनुगुणत्वे, तु, न, तत्संख्यादुराग्रहः ॥

अन्वयः

प्रमायाम् - in valid knowledge

यद् - that which

प्रत्यनीकम् - is an obstruction

भवेत् - is

(तत्) - that

न - not

हि - certainly

करणम् - the causal factor

प्रमित्यनुगणत्वे (प्रमाणे) - in the case that a means of acquiring knowledge is congruent with (leads to) valid knowledge,

तु - in contrast

न - not

तत्संख्यादुराग्रहः - insistence on its enumeration

That which obstructs knowledge that accords with truth certainly does not lead to valid knowledge. On the other hand, in the case that a means of acquiring knowledge leads to valid knowledge, here, there is no insistence on the enumeration of means.[50] (113)

---

50 Philosophical schools often go great lengths to enumerate the various methods of acquiring valid knowledge. Here, however, the author shifts the conversation to focus on the acquisition of valid knowledge, rather than on enumeration of methods.

अतोऽर्थापत्तिरित्यादेश्चेत् सिद्धान्ताऽविरोधिता ।
तदा बोधोपयुक्तत्वात् पृथगुक्ता प्रमाणता ॥११४॥

ato'rthāpattirityādeścet siddhāntā'virodhitā,
tadā bodhopayuktatvāt pṛthaguktā pramāṇatā.

पदच्छेदः - अतः, अर्थापत्तिरित्यादेः, चेत्, सिद्धान्ताऽविरोधिता, तदा, बोधोपयुक्तत्वात्, पृथक्, उक्ता, प्रमाणता ॥

अन्वयः

अतः - therefore

अर्थापत्तिरित्यादेः (प्रमाणजातस्य) - of postulation and the aggregate of other such means of knowledge

सिद्धान्ताऽविरोधिता - non-opposition to truth

(भवेत्) - is

चेत् - if

तदा - then

बोधोपयुक्तत्वात् - due to being useful in acquiring knowledge

पृथक् - independent

प्रमाणता - the quality of being a valid means of knowledge

उक्ता - is said

Therefore, if postulation and other such means of acquiring knowledge are not in opposition to truth, they are said to be independent means of valid knowledge, as they are useful in understanding truth. (114)

4.8 Erroneous Knowledge

भ्रान्तौ ख्यातिस्तु विज्ञेया चिदचित्ख्यातिसंज्ञका ।
प्रवृत्तिर्द्विविधा भ्रान्तेस्तस्मादेकान्तिको न हि ॥११५॥

bhrāntau khyātistu vijñeyā cidacitkhyātisaṃjñakā,
pravṛttirdvividhā bhrāntestasmādekāntiko na hi.

पदच्छेदः - भ्रान्तौ, ख्यातिः, तु, विज्ञेया, चिदचित्ख्यातिसंज्ञका, प्रवृत्तिः, द्विविधा, भ्रान्तेः, तस्मात्, एकान्तिकः, न, हि ॥

अन्वयः

भ्रान्तौ - in the subject of delusion

तु - indeed

चिदचित्ख्यातिसंज्ञका - to be of the designation of 'cidacit'

ख्यातिः - knowledge

विज्ञेया - should be known as

भ्रान्तेः - of delusion

द्विविधा - two types

प्रवृत्तिः - source (object)

तस्मात् - therefore

न - not

हि - certainly

एकान्तिकः - that which appears as one

In the subject of delusion, knowledge should be known as 'cidacitkhyāti'. Delusion has two types of sources; therefore, it certainly does not appear as one. (115)

पञ्चीकारो भवेद् यत्र सत्कार्यतोपपद्यते ।
अचित्ख्यातिर्मता तत्र शुक्त्यादौ रजतादिके ॥ ११६ ॥

pañcīkāro bhaved yatra satkāryatopapadyate,
acitkhyātirmatā tatra śuktyādau rajatādike.

पदच्छेद: - पञ्चीकार:, भवेत्, यत्र, सत्कार्यता, उपपद्यते । अचित्ख्याति:, मता, तत्र, शुक्त्यादौ, रजतादिके ॥

अन्वय:

यत्र - where

पञ्चीकार: - quintuplication

भवेत् - occurs

(अर्थात्) - in other words

सत्कार्यता - the creation of material objects

उपपद्यते - occurs

तत्र - there

अचित्ख्याति: - acitkhyāti

मता - is understood

(यथा) - such as

शुक्त्यादौ - when in shells and other such objects

रजतादिके - silver and other such items

(ज्ञाते) - are cognised

Among objects that are created as a result of quintuplication and satkāryatā, delusion is understood to take the form of acitkhyāti. An example of such delusion occurs when silver and other such items are cognised in shells and other such objects. (116)

ततो भिन्ने तु चित्ख्यातिर्वैपरीत्यं यदा भवेत् ।
यथाऽऽत्मसु जडत्वादि चेतनत्वं जडेषु च ॥ ११७॥

tato bhinne tu citkhyātirvaiparītyaṃ yadā bhavet,
yathā''tmasu jaḍatvādi cetanatvaṃ jaḍeṣu ca.

पदच्छेदः - ततः, भिन्ने, तु, चित्ख्यातिः, वैपरीत्यम्, यदा, भवेत्, यथाऽऽत्मसु, जडत्वादि, चेतनत्वम्, जडेषु च ॥

अन्वयः

ततः - from this

भिन्ने (विषये) - in a different subject

वैपरीत्यम् - delusion

यदा - when

(भवेत्) - occurs

(तदा) - then

चित्ख्यातिः - citkhyāti

भवेत् - occurs

यथा - such as

आत्मसु - in relation to the ātmans

जडत्वादि – non-sentience and other qualities

जडेषु – in relation to non-sentient objects

च - and

चेतनत्वम् - sentience

(मतम्) - one understands

Delusion concerning a subject other than that previously presented should be known as citkhyāti. An example of such delusion occurs when one understands non-sentience and other qualities to exist in the ātmans or when one understands sentience to exist in non-sentient objects. (117)

एवं परब्रह्मस्वामिनारायणप्रबोधित-ब्रह्मस्वरूपगुणातीतगुरुपरम्परोपबृंहित-
ब्रह्मविद्यालक्षणाऽक्षरपुरुषोत्तमदर्शनप्रतिपादके
साधुभद्रेशदासविरचिते
स्वामिनारायणसिद्धान्तसुधाऽऽख्ये शास्त्रेऽस्मिन्
समाप्तं प्रमाणधारा नाम
चतुर्थं प्रकरणम् ॥

In this way ends the fourth chapter, known as the 'Pramana dhārā', of Sadhu Bhadreshdas' *Svāminārāyaṇa-siddhānta-sudhā*, a text that substantiates the Akṣara-Puruṣottama Darśana, which is characterised as brahmavidyā, was taught by Parabrahman Swaminarayan, and has been fostered by the lineage of brahmasvarūpa, guṇātīta gurus.

Chapter 5

Māyā-dhārā

5.1 Introduction

The preceding three chapters discussed Akṣara and Puruṣottama, as well as the means to attaining knowledge of these two divine entities. The author now discuses māyā, the substance that prevents people from attaining this knowledge.

Māyā is the only one of the five ontological entities that is non-sentient. It is eternal but is constantly changing as its three qualities (sattva, rajas, and tamas) continually subdue each other. All things created in the universe are comprised of these three qualities of māyā in varying degrees. Māyā is thus known as one of the universe's material causes. Furthermore, it is known as the cause of ego, possessiveness, delusion, carelessness, and attachment. It also hinders spiritual knowledge and causes one to see Paramātman and the Akṣarabrahman guru as ordinary, rather than divine. In this way, it blocks liberation and causes perpetual return to the cycle of births and deaths.

The Akṣara-Puruṣottama Darśana, however, teaches that māyā can be overcome through association with the Akṣarabrahman guru. This chapter thus concludes by exalting such association and saying that, once the jīva crosses māyā through such association, it can offer unhindered bhakti to Parabrahman.

5.2 Benediction

The 'Māyā-dhārā' begins with an invocation to Akṣara and Puruṣottama. It exalts them as the two entities that govern māyā, the focus of this chapter.

त्रिगुणसाम्यवैषम्ये यदाधिपत्यसम्भवे।
वन्दे मायाऽधिपौ साक्षादक्षरपुरुषोत्तमौ ॥ ११८ ॥

triguṇasāmyavaiṣamye yadādhipatyasambhave,
vande māyā'dhipau sākṣādakṣarapuruṣottamau.

पदच्छेदः - त्रिगुणसाम्यवैषम्ये, यदाधिपत्यसम्भवे, वन्दे, मायाऽधिपौ, साक्षात्, अक्षरपुरुषोत्तमौ ॥

अन्वयः

त्रिगुणसाम्यवैषम्ये - in the balance and imbalance of māyā's three qualities

यदाधिपत्यसम्भवे - to those under whose rulership it comes to be

मायाऽधिपौ - to the controllers of māyā

साक्षात् - themselves

अक्षरपुरुषोत्तमौ - to Akṣara and Puruṣottama

वन्दे - I bow

I bow to the manifest forms of Akṣara and Puruṣottama, the rulers of māyā, under whose sovereignty māyā's three qualities attain balance and imbalance. (118)

5.3 Māyā's Nature & Form

माया त्रिगुणयुक्ता स्याद् ब्रह्मपरात्मशासिता।
परिणामवती नित्या विस्मयकारिणी जडा॥ ११९॥

māyā triguṇayuktā syād brahmaparātmaśāsitā,
pariṇāmavatī nityā vismayakāriṇī jaḍā.

पदच्छेदः - माया, त्रिगुणयुक्ता, स्यात्, ब्रह्मपरात्मशासिता, परिणामवती, नित्या, विस्मयकारिणी, जडा॥

अन्वयः

त्रिगुणयुक्ता - that which is of three qualities

माया - māyā

ब्रह्मपरात्मशासिता - that which is governed by Akṣara and Puruṣottama

स्यात् - is

(सा) - it

परिणामवती - changing

नित्या - eternal

जडा - non-sentient

विस्मयकारिणी च - and astounding

(स्यात्) - is

Māyā, which is of three qualities,[51] is governed by Akṣara and Puruṣottama. It is ever-changing, eternal, non-sentient, and astounding. (119)

51 See verse 123.

5.4 Māyā's Role in Creation and Transmigration

सृष्ट्युपादानभूतेयं हेतुरनादिसंसृतेः।
साधनात् परशक्तिश्च ममत्वाऽहन्त्वकारणम्॥ १२०॥

sṛṣṭyupādānabhūteyaṃ heturanādisaṃsṛteḥ,
sādhanāt paraśaktiśca mamatvā'hantvakāraṇam.

पदच्छेदः - सृष्ट्युपादानभूता, इयम्, हेतुः, अनादिसंसृतेः, साधनात्, परशक्तिः, च, ममत्वाऽहन्त्वकारणम्॥

अन्वयः

इयम् (माया) - this māyā

सृष्टि-उपादानभूता - is the material cause of creation

अनादिसंसृतेः - of the eternal cycle of birth and death

हेतुः - the cause

ममत्व-अहन्त्व-कारणम् - the cause of 'I-ness' and 'my-ness'

साधनात् च - and because it is an instrument

परशक्तिः - Paramātman's power

This māyā is the material cause of the world, the source of the eternal cycle of birth and death, and the impetus behind mamatva ('my-ness') and ahantva ('I-ness').[52] As an instrument, it is also one of Paramātman's many powers. (120)

52 Mamatva and ahantva, or 'my-ness' and 'I-ness', respectively, have been loosely translated as 'possessiveness' and 'ego' in this chapter's introduction.

अनाद्यज्ञानरूपेयं विक्षेपमोहकारिणी।
प्रमादो लौकिके रागः प्राकृता धीर्हरौ गुरौ॥ १२१॥

anādyajñānarūpeyaṃ vikṣepamohakāriṇī,
pramādo laukike rāgaḥ prākṛtā dhīrharau gurau.

पदच्छेदः - अनाद्यज्ञानरूपा, इयम्, विक्षेपमोहकारिणी, प्रमादः, लौकिके, रागः, प्राकृता, धीः, हरौ, गुरौ॥

अन्वयः

इयम् (माया) - this māyā

अनादि-अज्ञानरूपा - appears in the form of beginning-less ignorance

विक्षेपमोहकारिणी - is that which causes obstacles and delusion

लौकिके - in worldly objects

रागः - attachment

प्रमादः - carelessness

हरौ गुरौ (च) - and in Paramātman and the Akṣarabrahman guru

प्राकृता - worldly

धीः - disposition

(च) - and

(तया कार्यन्ते) - are caused by it

This māyā is characterised as ignorance that has no beginning. It engenders obstacles and delusion. Moreover, it instigates carelessness and attachment towards worldly objects and causes one to see Paramātman and the Akṣarabrahman guru as worldly figures. (121)

5.5 Māyā's Various Names

मायैव प्रकृतिः प्रोक्ता तमोऽन्धकारशब्दिता।
स्वभाववासनाद्याश्च तस्याः स्युर्विविधाऽभिधाः ॥ १२२ ॥

māyaiva prakṛtiḥ proktā tamo'ndhakārādiśabditā,
svabhāvavāsanādyāśca tasyāḥ syurvividhā'bhidhāḥ.

पदच्छेदः - माया, एव, प्रकृतिः, प्रोक्ता, तमोऽन्धकारशब्दिता, स्वभाववासनाद्याः, च, तस्याः, स्युः, विविधाऽभिधाः ॥

अन्वयः

माया - māyā

एव - indeed

प्रकृतिः - prakṛti

प्रोक्ता - is called

(सा) - it

तमोऽन्धकारशब्दिता - is referred to by the words tamas and andhakāra (darkness)

तस्याः - its

स्वभाववासनाद्याः - svabhāva (inherent nature), vāsanā (desire), etc.

च - and

विविधाऽभिधाः - various names

स्युः - are

Māyā is known as prakṛti. It is also referred to by the words tamas and andhakāra (darkness). Furthermore, it is known by labels such as svabhāva (inherent nature) and vāsanā (desire). (122)

5.6 Māyā's Three Qualities

सत्त्वं रजस्तमश्चेति त्रयः स्युः प्रकृतेर्गुणाः।
अन्योऽन्याऽभिभवाश्चैव मिथः संमिश्रिताः सदा॥ १२३॥

sattvaṃ rajastamaśceti trayaḥ syuḥ prakṛterguṇāḥ,
anyo'nyā'bhibhavāścaiva mithaḥ saṃmiśritāḥ sadā.

<u>पदच्छेदः</u> - सत्त्वम्, रजः, तमः, च, इति, त्रयः, स्युः, प्रकृतेः, गुणाः, अन्योऽन्याऽभिभवाः, च, एव, मिथः, संमिश्रिताः, सदा॥

<u>अन्वयः</u>

सत्त्वम् - sattva
रजः - rajas
तमः - tamas
च - and
इति - the aforementioned
त्रयः - three
प्रकृतेः - māyā's
गुणाः - qualities
स्युः - are
(ते) - they
सदा - ever
अन्योऽन्याऽभिभवाः - subdued by one another
च - and
मिथः - mutually
संमिश्रिताः - blended
एव - indeed

Sattva, rajas, and tamas are māyā's three qualities. These qualities are ever subdued by one another and are mutually intertwined. (123)

5.7 Overcoming Māyā

गुणानेतानतीत्य त्रीन् साधर्म्यं ब्रह्मणा भवेत्।
गुणातीतं गुरुं प्राप्य भक्तिश्च परमात्मनि॥ १२४॥

guṇānetānatītya trīn sādharmyaṃ brahmaṇā bhavet,
guṇātītaṃ guruṃ prāpya bhaktiśca paramātmani.

पदच्छेदः - गुणान्, एतान्, अतीत्य, त्रीन्, साधर्म्यम्, ब्रह्मणा, भवेत्, गुणातीतम्, गुरुम्, प्राप्य, भक्तिः, च, परमात्मनि॥

अन्वयः

गुणातीतम् - one who is above māyā's qualities

गुरुम् - guru

प्राप्य - having attained

एतान् - these

त्रीन् - three

गुणान् - qualities

अतीत्य - having transcended

ब्रह्मणा (सह) - with Akṣarabrahman

साधर्म्यम् - likeness

भवेत् - can occur

परमात्मनि - in Paramātman

च - and

भक्तिः - bhakti

(भवेत्) - can occur

Having attained the guṇātīta guru and transcended these three qualities of māyā, one can achieve likeness with Akṣarabrahman and offer bhakti to Paramātman. (124)

एवं परब्रह्मस्वामिनारायणप्रबोधित-ब्रह्मस्वरूपगुणातीतगुरुपरम्परोपबृंहित-
ब्रह्मविद्यालक्षणाऽक्षरपुरुषोत्तमदर्शनप्रतिपादके
साधुभद्रेशदासविरचिते
स्वामिनारायणसिद्धान्तसुधाऽऽख्ये शास्त्रेऽस्मिन्
समाप्तं मायाधारा नाम
पञ्चमं प्रकरणम् ॥

In this way ends the fifth chapter, known as the 'Māyā-dhārā', of Sadhu Bhadreshdas' *Svāminārāyaṇa-siddhānta-sudhā*, a text that substantiates the Akṣara-Puruṣottama Darśana, which is characterised as brahmavidyā, was taught by Parabrahman Swaminarayan, and has been fostered by the lineage of brahmasvarūpa, guṇātīta gurus.

Chapter 6

Jīva-dhārā

6.1 Introduction

The previous chapter discussed māyā, the entity that prevents a person from obtaining valid knowledge. It also explained how one can overcome māyā. The next two chapters describe the jīva and īśvara, the entities that māyā restricts and the beings that overcome māyā to attain liberation.

The present chapter takes up the jīva as its subject of inquiry. It first offers an etymological analysis of the term 'jīva', arguing that it is known by this term because it brings the body to life and is sentient in its own respect. The author then describes the jīva's three bodies and states of being that characterise its existence so long as it is bound by māyā. He also states, however, that the jīva is inherently separate from and superior to these three bodies and states of being. Upon liberation, it sheds its bodies and states of being and takes upon a fourth body (the brāhmavigraha) and enjoys a fourth state of being (brāhmi sthiti).

The jīva can never act on its own. Paramātman, however, graces it with the power to desire, know, and act; moreover, he grants it a body through which it can exercise these faculties.

The author concludes this chapter with a discussion of the

jīva's inherent nature. He posits, first, that the jīva is eternal. It is said to be born and die, but this is only due to its association and disassociation with various bodies during the cycle of transmigration. Furthermore, the jīva resides within the body and empowers its functions, yet is separate from it. It is inherently blissful and also embodies bliss. Nonetheless, the level of bliss it enjoys is much lesser than the bliss of Akṣarabrahman and Parabrahman. Lastly, the author notes that the jīva is intrinsically pure; even though it is bound by māyā, it remains fundamentally unadulterated.

Indeed, understanding the jīva's nature is essential to the Akṣara-Puruṣottama Darśana's most significant spiritual praxis, which involves eliminating body consciousness, realising one's identity as the jīva, and attaining cognitive oneness with Akṣarabrahman. According to the Akṣara-Puruṣottama Darśana, this realisation is the only way to offer unhindered bhakti to Parabrahman and thus secure one's liberation.

6.2 Benediction

The author begins this sixth chapter by bowing to Akṣara and Puruṣottama, the entities that sustain the jīva and compassionately guide it to liberation.

इच्छाज्ञानक्रियाशक्तेर्जीवानां यः प्रदायकः ।
वन्दे तं मुक्तिदातारमक्षरपुरुषोत्तमम् ॥ १२५ ॥

icchājñānakriyāśakterjīvānāṃ yaḥ pradāyakaḥ,
vande taṃ muktidātāramakṣarapuruṣottamam.

पदच्छेदः - इच्छाज्ञानक्रियाशक्तेः, जीवानाम्, यः, प्रदायकः, वन्दे, तम्, मुक्तिदातारम्, अक्षरपुरुषोत्तमम् ॥

अन्वयः

यः - the entity which

जीवानाम् - to the jīva

इच्छाज्ञानक्रियाशक्तेः - of the strength to desire, know, and act

प्रदायकः - the giver

तम् - to this entity

मुक्तिदातारम् - the granter of liberation

अक्षरपुरुषोत्तमम् - Akṣara-Puruṣottama

वन्दे - I bow

I bow to Akṣara-Puruṣottama, who gives the jīva the strength to desire, know, and act and grants the jīva liberation. (125)

6.3 An Etymological Analysis

जीवयति स्वदेहं यो जीवति च स्वयं यतः।
तस्माद्धि चेतनाऽऽत्माऽयं जीव इति प्रकीर्तितः॥ १२६ ॥

jīvayati svadehaṃ yo jīvati ca svayaṃ yataḥ,
tasmāddhi cetanā''tmā'yaṃ jīva iti prakīrtitaḥ.

पदच्छेदः - जीवयति, स्वदेहम्, यः, जीवति, च, स्वयम्, यतः, तस्मात्, हि, चेतनाऽऽत्मा, अयम्, जीवः, इति, प्रकीर्तितः॥

अन्वयः

यतः - because
स्वयम् - itself
जीवति - lives
यः - that which
च - and
स्वदेहम् - its body
जीवयति - brings to life
तस्माद् - due to this
हि - certainly
अयम् - this
चेतनाऽऽत्मा - the sentient ātman
जीवः - jīva
इति - the aforementioned
प्रकीर्तितः - is called

This sentient ātman is called the jīva because it lives and enables the body to live.[53] (126)

53 The Saṃskṛta root verb 'jīva' means 'to live'. The causitive form of this verb means 'to make live'. (Sāyaṇācārya 109)

6.4 The Jīva's Three Bodies & States of Being

स्थूलमेकं तथा सूक्ष्मं तृतीयं कारणं मतम्।
तस्य त्रीणि शरीराणि यद्बन्धात् संसृतिं गतः ॥ १२७ ॥

sthūlamekaṃ tathā sūkṣmaṃ tṛtīyaṃ kāraṇaṃ matam,
tasya trīṇi śarīrāṇi yadbandhāt saṃsṛtiṃ gataḥ.

पदच्छेदः - स्थूलम्, एकम्, तथा, सूक्ष्मम्, तृतीयम्, कारणम्, मतम्, तस्य, त्रीणि, शरीराणि, यद्बन्धात्, संसृतिम्, गतः ॥

अन्वयः

तस्य - its (the jīva's)

एकम् - one

स्थूलम् - physical

तथा - and

सूक्ष्मम् - subtle

तृतीयम् - third

(च) - and

कारणम् - causal

(इति) - the aforementioned

त्रीणि - three

शरीराणि - bodies

मतम् - are recognised

यद्बन्धात् - due to whose bondage

(जीवः) - the jīva

संसृतिम् - the cycle of birth and death

गतः - attains

The physical, subtle, and causal are recognised as the jīva's three bodies. The bonds of these bodies cause the jīva to attain the cycle of birth and death. (127)

Once a person who has attained liberation deceases, the jīva sheds the three bodies mentioned above and takes upon a fourth body, a divine figure that is known as a brāhmavigraha.

एतद्देहत्रयाद् भिन्नो जीवात्माऽयं सनातनः।
लभते ब्रह्मलोके तु चतुर्थं ब्राह्मविग्रहम्॥ १२८॥

etaddehatrayād bhinno jīvātmā'yaṃ sanātanaḥ,
labhate brahmaloke tu caturthaṃ brāhmavigraham.

<u>पदच्छेदः</u> - एतद्देहत्रयात्, भिन्नः, जीवात्मा, अयम्, सनातनः, लभते, ब्रह्मलोके, तु, चतुर्थम्, ब्राह्मविग्रहम्॥

<u>अन्वयः</u>

अयम् - this

जीवात्मा - jīvātman

एतद्देहत्रयाद् - from these three bodies

भिन्नः - that which is distinct

सनातनः (च) - and that which is eternal

ब्रह्मलोके - in Akṣaradhāman

तु - moreover

(सः) - it

चतुर्थम् - fourth

ब्राह्मविग्रहम् - brāhmavigraha

लभते - attains

This jīvātman[54] is distinct from these three bodies and is eternal. In Akṣaradhāman, it attains a fourth body, which is known as a brāhmavigraha.[55] (128)

---

54 The jīva can also be known, interchangeably, as the 'ātman' and the 'jīvātman'. Often, it is translated as 'soul'.

55 See verse 173.

जागरणं तथा स्वप्नः सुषुप्तिश्चेति बुध्यते।
बद्धानां न तु मुक्तानां तेषां ब्रह्मणि संस्थितेः ॥ १२९ ॥

jāgaraṇaṃ tathā svapnaḥ suṣuptiśceti budhyate,
baddhānāṃ na tu muktānāṃ teṣāṃ brahmaṇi saṃsthiteḥ.

पदच्छेदः - जागरणम्, तथा, स्वप्नः, सुषुप्तिः, च, इति, बुध्यते, बद्धानाम्, न, तु, मुक्तानाम्, तेषाम्, ब्रह्मणि, संस्थितेः ॥

अन्वयः

जागरणम् - waking

तथा - and

स्वप्नः - dream

सुषुप्तिः - deep sleep

च - and

इति - the aforementioned

(जीवस्य) - the jīva's

(अवस्थाः) - states

बुध्यते - are known

(एताः) - these states

बद्धानाम् - of bound jīvas

न - not

तु - however

मुक्तानाम् - of liberated jīvas

तेषां ब्रह्मणि संस्थितेः - due to their qualitative oneness with Akṣarabrahman.

Waking, dream, and deep sleep are the jīva's three states. These states apply to bound jīvas. However, they do not apply to released jīvas, as such entities have attained qualitative oneness with Akṣarabrahman. (129)

One who has attained liberation rises above these three states and enjoys a fourth state, that of oneness with Akṣarabrahman.

तूर्याऽवस्था स्थितिर्ब्राह्मी मुक्तिरूपा प्रकीर्तिता।
जीवतोऽपि भवेल्लभ्या जाग्रदादित्रयात् परा॥ १३०॥

tūryā'vasthā sthitirbrāhmī muktirūpā prakīrtitā,
jīvato'pi bhavellabhyā jāgradāditrayāt parā.

पदच्छेदः - तूर्याऽवस्था, स्थितिः, ब्राह्मी, मुक्तिरूपा, प्रकीर्तिता, जीवतः, अपि, भवेत्, लभ्या, जाग्रदादित्रयात्, परा॥

अन्वयः

जाग्रदादित्रयात् - from the waking, etc., three states.

परा - the transcendent

ब्राह्मी स्थितिः - the state of oneness with Akṣarabrahman

प्रकीर्तिता - known as

(एषा) - this

मुक्तिरूपा - the form of liberation

तूर्याऽवस्था - the fourth state

जीवतः - while being alive

अपि - despite

लभ्या - attainable

भवेत् - can be

The state of being one with Akṣarabrahman transcends the three states of waking, dream, and deep sleep. This condition is known as the state of liberation. This fourth state can be attained while living.[56] (130)

56 The Akṣara-Puruṣottama Darśana holds that there are two types of liberation: jivan-mukti (that which is experienced while a person is alive) and videha-mukti (that which is experienced after a person deceases). The state of realisation enjoyed in both are identical. For more, see verses 169-70, 171-78.

6.5 How Paramātman Empowers the Jīva

इच्छाशक्तिः परात्लब्धा ज्ञानशक्तिस्तथैव च।
क्रियाशक्तिः परात्लब्धा जीवेन कृपया प्रभोः ॥ १३१ ॥

icchāśaktiḥ parāllabdhā jñānaśaktistathaiva ca,
kriyāśaktiḥ parāllabdhā jīvena kṛpayā prabhoḥ.

पदच्छेदः - इच्छाशक्तिः, परात्, लब्धा, ज्ञानशक्तिः, तथा, एव, च, क्रियाशक्तिः, परात्, लब्धा, जीवेन, कृपया, प्रभोः ॥

अन्वयः

प्रभोः कृपया - by Paramātman's grace

जीवेन - by the jīva

परात् (परमात्मतः) - from Paramātman

इच्छाशक्तिः - the ability to desire

लब्धा - is acquired

तथा एव - in the same way

ज्ञानशक्तिः - the ability to know

क्रियाशक्तिः च - and the ability to act

परात् (परमात्मतः) - from Paramātman

लब्धा - is acquired

From Paramātman, and by Paramātman's grace, the jīva acquires the ability to desire, know, and act. (131)

6.6 The Jīva's Inherent Nature

जन्म नास्ति मृतिर्नास्ति नित्य आत्मा सनातनः।
देहयोगविभागाभ्यां जातो मृतोऽयमुच्यते॥ १३२॥

janma nāsti mṛtirnāsti nitya ātmā sanātanaḥ,
dehayogavibhāgābhyāṃ jāto mṛto'yamucyate.

पदच्छेदः - जन्म, न, अस्ति, मृतिः, न, अस्ति, नित्यः, आत्मा, सनातनः, देहयोगविभागाभ्याम्, जातः, मृतः, अयम्, उच्यते॥

अन्वयः

(जीवस्य) - the jīva's

जन्म - birth

न अस्ति - does not occur

मृतिः - death

नास्तिः - does not occur

आत्मा - the ātman

सनातनः - that which exists forever

नित्यः - that which is eternal

(अस्ति) - is

अयम् - this (the jīva)

देहयोगविभागाभ्याम् - through association and disassociation with the body

जातः - born

मृतः - dead

(इति) - the aforementioned

उच्यते - is said to be

The jīva is not born, nor does it die. It is eternal and ever-lasting. It is said to undergo birth and death merely due to its association and disassociation with the body. (132)

देहस्थो देहभिन्नोऽयं देहेन्द्रियप्रकाशकः।
देहादेस्तं विना नैव स्वकार्येषु प्रवर्तनम्॥ १३३॥

dehastho dehabhinno'yaṃ dehendriyaprakāśakaḥ,
dehādestaṃ vinā naiva svakāryeṣu pravartanam.

पदच्छेदः - देहस्थः, देहभिन्नः, अयम्, देहेन्द्रियप्रकाशकः, देहादेः, तम्, विना, न, एव, स्वकार्येषु, प्रवर्तनम्॥

अन्वयः

अयम् (जीवः) - this jīva

देहस्थः - that which resides in the body

(अपि) - however

देहभिन्नः - that which is separate from the body

देहेन्द्रियप्रकाशकः - that which illuminates the body and the senses

तम् - it

विना - without

देहादेः - of the body and other [instruments that make up the physical being]

स्वकार्येषु - in their respective tasks

प्रवर्तनम् - engagement

न एव - certainly is not

(शक्यम्) - possible

The jīva is distinct from the body, despite dwelling in it. It illuminates the body and the senses. Indeed, neither the body nor the senses can engage in their respective tasks in its absence. (133)

सुखी च सुखरूपोऽयं शास्त्रैः परिकीर्तितः।
सुखाच्चाऽस्य समुत्कृष्टं सुखं ब्रह्मपरात्मनोः॥ १३४॥

sukhī ca sukharūpo'yaṃ śāstraiḥ parikīrtitaḥ,
sukhāccā'sya samutkṛṣṭaṃ sukhaṃ brahmaparātmanoḥ.

पदच्छेदः - सुखी, च, सुखरूपः, अयम्, शास्त्रैः, परिकीर्तितः, सुखात्, च, अस्य, समुत्कृष्टम्, सुखम्, ब्रह्मपरात्मनोः॥

अन्वयः

शास्त्रैः - by the śāstras

अयम् (जीवः) - this jīva

सुखी - blissful

सुखरूपः - that which embodies bliss

च - and

परिकीर्तितः - is described

अस्य (जीवस्य) सुखात् - than this jīva's bliss

च - and

ब्रह्मपरात्मनोः - Akṣarabrahman's and Paramātman's

सुखम् - happiness

समुत्कृष्टम् - far greater

The śāstras describe that the jīva is blissful and that it embodies bliss. However, they also state that the happiness of Akṣarabrahman and Paramātman is far greater than that of the jīva. (134)

जीवात्मा नित्यशुद्धोऽस्ति मायामलविवर्जितः।
आवरकाऽपि माया तु जीवाऽन्तर्नैव गच्छति॥ १३५॥

jīvātmā nityaśuddho'sti māyāmalavivarjitaḥ,
āvarakā'pi māyā tu jīvā'ntarnaiva gacchati.

पदच्छेदः - जीवात्मा, नित्यशुद्धः, अस्ति, मायामलविवर्जितः, आवरका, अपि, माया, तु, जीवाऽन्तः, न, एव, गच्छति॥

अन्वयः

जीवात्मा - the jīvātman

नित्यशुद्धः - that which is eternally pure

मायामलविवर्जितः - that which is untouched by impurity in the form of māyā

अस्ति - is

आवरका - that which conceals

माया - māyā

अपि - even

जीवाऽन्तः - inside of the jīva

तु - yet

न एव - absolutely does not

गच्छति - go

The jīva is eternally pure and untouched by impurity in the form of māyā. Even though māyā conceals the jīva, it is unable to penetrate it. (135)

एवं परब्रह्मस्वामिनारायणप्रबोधित-ब्रह्मस्वरूपगुणातीतगुरुपरम्परोपबृंहित-
ब्रह्मविद्यालक्षणाऽक्षरपुरुषोत्तमदर्शनप्रतिपादके
साधुभद्रेशदासविरचिते
स्वामिनारायणसिद्धान्तसुधाऽऽख्ये शास्त्रेऽस्मिन्
समाप्तं जीवधारा नाम
षष्ठं प्रकरणम् ॥

In this way ends the sixth chapter, known as the 'Jiva-dhārā', of Sadhu Bhadreshdas' *Svāminārāyaṇa-siddhānta-sudhā*, a text that substantiates the Akṣara-Puruṣottama Darśana, which is characterised as brahmavidyā, was taught by Parabrahman Swaminarayan, and has been fostered by the lineage of brahmasvarūpa, guṇātīta gurus.

Chapter 7

Īśvara-dhārā

7.1 Introduction

Īśvaras are ontologically distinct from and superior to jīvas. In fact, they get their name, 'īśvara', due to the distinct virtues or enhanced faculties (aiśvarya) that they enjoy and employ in overseeing creation. However, like jīvas, they are sentient, eternal, and bound by māyā; they are also many in number. Furthermore, the īśvaras experience the fruit of their karma. Although they possess three bodies and enjoy three states, the names of their bodies and states are different from those of the jīvas. Namely, their three bodies are the virāṭ, sūtrātmā, and avyākṛta; their three states are creation, sustenance, and dissolution. Again like the jīvas, they remain eternally distinct from all of their bodies and states.

The īśvaras yearn for liberation. However, liberation can only be attained by overcoming māyā. Such transcendence, moreover, is only possible through the association of the manifest, Akṣarabrahman guru. Therefore, the īśvaras take birth in human form in order to enjoy the company of this guru and attain release from the transmigratory cycle.

7.2 An Etymological Analysis

ऐश्वर्यादीश्वरः प्रोक्तो जीवाद् भिन्नः स्वरूपतः ।
ज्ञानं ज्ञाता च नित्यश्च मायाबद्धोऽस्त्यनादितः ॥ १३६ ॥

aiśvaryādīśvaraḥ prokto jīvād bhinnaḥ svarūpataḥ,
jñānaṃ jñātā ca nityaśca māyābaddho'styanāditaḥ.

पदच्छेदः - ऐश्वर्यात्, ईश्वरः, प्रोक्तः, जीवात्, भिन्नः, स्वरूपतः, ज्ञानम्, ज्ञाता, च, नित्यः, च, मायाबद्धः, अस्ति, अनादितः ॥

अन्वयः

स्वरूपतः - ontologically
जीवाद् - from the jīva
भिन्नः - distinct
ऐश्वर्याद् - due to its powers
(च) - and
ईश्वरः - the īśvara
प्रोक्तः - is called
(एतस्य स्वरूपम्) - its form
ज्ञानम् - wisdom
(एषः) - it
ज्ञाता - knower
च - and
नित्यः - eternal
च - and
अनादितः - eternally
मायाबद्धः - bound by māyā
अस्ति - is

The īśvara is ontologically distinct from the jīva. It is known as 'īśvara' due to its significant powers.[57] It embodies wisdom and is the knower. It is eternal and has always been bound by māyā. (136)

57 The word 'īśvara' comes from the Saṃskṛta root verb 'īśa', which expresses the act of sovereignty (Sāyaṇācārya 231); the īśvaras' nomenclature thus signifies that they possess enhanced divine faculties that facilitate their governance of the brahmāṇḍas through such tasks as creation, sustenance, and destruction.

7.3 The Īśvara's Nature & Form

अत्यन्तमसमर्थोऽपि ब्रह्मणः परब्रह्मणः ।
जीवाच्छ्रेष्ठतयोक्तोऽयमनाद्यैश्वर्यहेतुतः ॥ १३७ ॥

atyantamasamartho'pi brahmaṇaḥ parabrahmaṇaḥ,
jīvācchreṣṭhatayokto'yamanādyaiśvaryahetutaḥ.

पदच्छेदः - अत्यन्तम्, असमर्थः, अपि, ब्रह्मणः, परब्रह्मणः, जीवात्, श्रेष्ठतया, उक्तः, अयम्, अनाद्यैश्वर्यहेतुतः ॥

अन्वयः

अयम् - this (the īśvara)

अनादि-ऐश्वर्य-हेतुतः - due to the eternal possession of divine faculties

जीवात् - than the jīva

श्रेष्ठतया - as being greater

उक्तः - is described

अपि - although

ब्रह्मणः - compared to Akṣarabrahman

परब्रह्मणः (च) - and compared to Parabrahman

अत्यन्तम् - extremely

असमर्थः - insignificant

(अस्ति) - is

Although the īśvara is described as being transcendent to the jīva due to its eternal powers, it is exceptionally insignificant when compared to Akṣarabrahman and Parabrahman. (137)

स्वकर्मफलभोक्ताऽयं ज्ञेयोऽच्छेद्यादिलक्षणः।
मोक्षाऽर्होऽनेकसंख्याकश्चेतनोऽणुः शरीरभाक्॥ १३८॥

svakarmaphalabhoktā'yaṃ jñeyo'cchedyādilakṣaṇaḥ,
mokṣā'rho'nekasaṃkhyākaścetano'ṇuḥ śarīrabhāk.

<u>पदच्छेदः</u> - स्वकर्मफलभोक्ता, अयम्, ज्ञेयः, अच्छेद्यादिलक्षणः, मोक्षाऽर्हः, अनेकसंख्याकः, चेतनः, अणुः, शरीरभाक्॥

<u>अन्वयः</u>

अयम् - this (īśvara)

स्वकर्मफलभोक्ता - that which is the experiencer of the fruits of its karmas

अच्छेद्यादिलक्षणः - that which possesses qualities such as indivisibility, etc.

मोक्षाऽर्हः - that which is entitled to liberation

चेतनः - that which is sentient

अणुः - that which is minute

शरीरभाक् - and attains a material body

अनेकसङ्ख्याकः - that which is numerous

ज्ञेयः - should be known as

The īśvara experiences the fruits of its karmas. It possesses qualities such as indivisibility and is entitled to liberation. It is minute, sentient, and attains a material body. There are countless such īśvaras. (138)

7.4 The Īśvara's Three Bodies & States of Being

विराडथ च सूत्रात्मा तृतीयोऽव्याकृतस्तथा।
ईश्वरस्य त्रयो देहाः सहजानन्दबोधिताः ॥ १३९ ॥

virāḍatha ca sūtrātmā tṛtīyo'vyākṛtastathā,
īśvarasya trayo dehāḥ sahajānandabodhitāḥ.

पदच्छेदः - विराट्, अथ, च, सूत्रात्मा, तृतीयः, अव्याकृतः, तथा, ईश्वरस्य, त्रयः, देहाः, सहजानन्दबोधिताः ॥

अन्वयः

अथ - as follows

विराट् - virāṭ

सूत्रात्मा - sūtrātmā

तथा च - and

तृतीयः - the third

अव्याकृतः - avyākṛta

(इति) - the aforementioned

ईश्वरस्य - the īśvara's

त्रयः - three

देहाः - bodies

सहजानन्दप्रबोधिताः - taught by Sahajanand (Swaminarayan)

Sahajanand (Swaminarayan) taught that the bodies of the īśvara are the virāṭ, sūtrātmā, and the third, the avyākṛta. (139)

उत्पत्तिश्च स्थितिश्चैव प्रलयश्चेति यत् त्रयम्।
तदवस्थास्तु विज्ञेया यया बद्धोऽनुतिष्ठति॥ १४०॥

utpattiśca sthitiścaiva pralayaśceti yat trayam,
tadavasthāstu vijñeyā yayā baddho'nutiṣṭhati.

पदच्छेदः - उत्पत्तिः, च, स्थितिः, च, एव, प्रलयः, च, इति, यत्, त्रयम्, तदवस्थाः, तु, विज्ञेयाः, यया, बद्धः, अनुतिष्ठति॥

अन्वयः

उत्पत्तिः - creation

च - and

स्थितिः - sustenance

च - and

प्रलयः - destruction

च - and

एव - indeed

इति - the aforementioned

यद् - that

त्रयम् - group of three

तदवस्थाः - its (the īśvara's) states of being

तु - indeed

विज्ञेयाः - should be understood

यया - that by which

(ईश्वरः) - the īśvara

बद्धः - bound

अनुतिष्ठति - remains

Creation, sustenance, and destruction are the īśvara's three states of being. The īśvara remains bound by these states. (140).

एवं परब्रह्मस्वामिनारायणप्रबोधित-ब्रह्मस्वरूपगुणातीतगुरुपरम्परोपबृंहित-
ब्रह्मविद्यालक्षणाऽक्षरपुरुषोत्तमदर्शनप्रतिपादके
साधुभद्रेशदासविरचिते
स्वामिनारायणसिद्धान्तसुधाऽऽख्ये शास्त्रेऽस्मिन्
समाप्तमीश्वरधारा नाम
सप्तमं प्रकरणम् ॥

In this way ends the seventh chapter, known as the 'Īśvara-dhārā', of Sadhu Bhadreshdas' *Svāminārāyaṇa-siddhānta-sudhā*, a text that substantiates the Akṣara-Puruṣottama Darśana, which is characterised as brahmavidyā, was taught by Parabrahman Swaminarayan, and has been fostered by the lineage of brahmasvarūpa, guṇātīta gurus.

Chapter 8

Sādhana-dhārā

8.1 Introduction

Chapters 2 through 7 of this book discussed Akṣara and Puruṣottama's greatness; they also discussed the pramāṇas, or the tools one can use to understand this greatness, and māyā, the primary force that hinders such understanding. These chapters then discussed the jīva and īśvara, the two entities that māyā obstructs.

Now, the text moves forth to describe how jīvas and īśvaras can free themselves of māyā and attain liberation through spiritual endeavour, or sādhana. The primary endeavour described here is the attainment of brahmabhāva, an undertaking that encompasses all other spiritual practices. Brahmabhāva describes the state of having attained oneness with Akṣarabrahman. This condition involves 1) believing that which the Akṣarabrahman guru believes; 2) acting virtuously, just as this guru; and 3) engaging one's physical being in Paramātman's bhakti, as this guru has also done.

The author then explains that attaining oneness with Akṣarabrahman is needed for perfecting bhakti. He goes on to describe ekāntika dharma, or bhāgavata dharma, which is defined as bhakti that is accompanied by dharma, jñāna, and vairāgya. Describing each of ekāntika dharma's facets, he explains that dharma is comprised of actions that fall in accordance with Paramātman's and the Akṣarabrahman guru's ordinances; jñāna is an understanding of one's congruence with Akṣarabrahman; vairāgya is detachment from all except for Akṣara and Purushotam; and bhakti is intense love for Paramātman and the guru. As the foremost of these four endeavours, bhakti manifests in nine ways. However, the greatest forms of bhakti are those that are centred on the manifest form of Paramātman. The author thus states that, after Parabrahman Swaminarayan's passing, one should offer bhakti to God through the Akṣarabrahman guru, through whom God manifests.

The chapter goes on to enumerate specific spiritual practices that the devotee is to undergo to obtain the guru's grace, which is essential for success on the spiritual path. The author concludes by stating that believing oneself to be brahmarūpa, or one with the Akṣarabrahman guru, is the foremost amongst these endeavours.

8.2 Benediction

The Sādhana-dhārā begins with a prayer to Parabrahman Swaminarayan and the Akṣarabrahman guru. Along with offering obeisance, this prayer also explains the essence of the Akṣara-Puruṣottama Darśana's praxis and prays that the key aspects of this praxis may be imbibed.

साक्षाद्ब्रह्मस्वरूपे प्रकटगुरुवरे प्रीतिकाष्ठां विधाय
सङ्गेन स्वात्ममध्ये स्वयमपि च तथा ब्रह्मभावं प्रधाय।
कार्या तत्रैव भक्त्या प्रकटहरिसुधीर्दिव्यभावं निधाय
सेव्यो ब्रह्मस्थदेवो भवभयतरणे स्वामिनारायणोऽयम्॥ १४१॥

sākṣādbrahmasvarūpe prakaṭaguruvare prītikāṣṭhāṃ vidhāya,
saṅgena svātmamadhye svayamapi ca tathā brahmabhāvaṃ pradhāya.
kāryā tatraiva bhaktyā prakaṭaharisudhīrdivyabhāvaṃ nidhāya
sevyo brahmasthadevo bhavabhayataraṇe svāminārāyaṇo'yam.

पदच्छेदः - साक्षाद्ब्रह्मस्वरूपे, प्रकटगुरुवरे, प्रीतिकाष्ठाम्, विधाय, सङ्गेन, स्वात्ममध्ये, स्वयम्, अपि, च, तथा, ब्रह्मभावम्, प्रधाय, कार्या, तत्र, एव, भक्त्या, प्रकटहरिसुधीः, दिव्यभावम्, निधाय, सेव्यः, ब्रह्मस्थदेवः, भवभयतरणे, स्वामिनारायणः, अयम्॥

अन्वयः

साक्षाद्ब्रह्मस्वरूपे प्रकटगुरुवरे - within the manifest, brahmasvarūpa guru

प्रीतिकाष्ठाम् - intense love

विधाय - having cultivated

(तस्य) सङ्गेन च - and through the guru's association

स्वात्ममध्ये - within one's ātman

स्वयम् अपि - oneself also

ब्रह्मभावम् - brahmabhāva

प्रधाय - having established

तथा - and

तत्र एव - there indeed

भक्त्या - with devotion

प्रकटगुरुहरिसुधीः - belief that the manifest guru is the form of God

कार्या - should be cultivated

दिव्यभावं च - and the understanding of inherent divinity

निधाय - having established

भवभयतरणे - to overcome the fear of saṃsāra

ब्रह्मस्थदेवः - the God that resides in Akṣarabrahman

अयं स्वामिनारायणः - this manifest [form of] Swaminarayan

सेव्यः - should be served

To overcome the fear of saṃsāra, one should serve the manifest Swaminarayan, who resides within the Akṣarabrahman guru. One should do so upon cultivating intense love for the manifest, Akṣarabrahman guru; establishing brahmabhāva in one's ātman through this guru's association; and offering bhakti with the understanding that the guru is inherently divine and is the very form of God. (141)

आज्ञोपासनसद्भावपक्षा हि जीवजीवनम्।
देहि निश्चलनिष्ठार्थमक्षरपुरुषोत्तमे॥ १४२॥

ājñopāsanasadbhāvapakṣā hi jīvajīvanam,
dehi niścalaniṣṭhārthamakṣarapuruṣottame.

पदच्छेदः - आज्ञोपासनसद्भावपक्षाः, हि, जीवजीवनम्, देहि, निश्चलनिष्ठार्थम्, अक्षरपुरुषोत्तमे॥

अन्वयः

आज्ञोपासनसद्भावपक्षाः - ājñā (obedience to divine ordinances), upāsanā (worshipful faith), sadbhāva (fraternity) and pakṣa (loyalty)

हि - indeed

जीवजीवनम् - the jīva's life force

(अतः) - therefore

(हे गुरुहरे!) - O Guru-hari!

अक्षरपुरुषोत्तमे - in Akṣara-Puruṣottama

निश्चलनिष्ठार्थम् - for unwavering conviction

(एतान्) - these qualities

(नः) - upon us

देहि - bestow

Ājñā (obedience to divine ordinances), upāsanā (worshipful faith), sadbhāva (fraternity), and pakṣa (loyalty) indeed are the jīva's life force.[58] Therefore, O Guru-hari! Kindly bestow these qualities upon me so that I may develop unwavering conviction in Akṣara-Puruṣottama. (142)

58 Bhadreshdas writes at the *Svāminārāyaṇa-siddhānta-sudhā*'s outset that his work is a meditation on the teachings of Swaminarayan and the Akṣarabrahman gurus (p.5). In this spirit, the coagulation of the four spiritual practices described above stems from the ministry of Brahmasvarūpa Shastriji Maharaj, who explained that these four practices are vital to the jīva's spiritual progress; he referred to them as the jīva's very life force, or that which helps the jīva spiritually thrive and attain resolute conviction.

8.3 Attaining Oneness with Akṣarabrahman

Having invoked God's and the guru's blessings, the author now explains the importance of divine approval, grace, and attaining oneness with Akṣarabrahman in mastering the spiritual endeavours.

दयार्णवः कृपासाध्यः प्रसादात् सुलभा कृपा।
ब्रह्मभावात् प्रसीदेच्च ह्यक्षरपुरुषोत्तमः ॥ १४३ ॥

dayārṇavaḥ kṛpāsādhyaḥ prasādāt sulabhā kṛpā,
brahmabhāvāt prasīdecca hyakṣarapuruṣottamaḥ.

पदच्छेदः - दयार्णवः, कृपासाध्यः, प्रसादात्, सुलभा, कृपा, ब्रह्मभावात्, प्रसीदेत्, च, हि, अक्षरपुरुषोत्तमः ॥

अन्वयः

अक्षरपुरुषोत्तमः - Akṣara-Puruṣottama

कृपासाध्यः - that which is attainable through grace

दयार्णवः - that which is comparable to an ocean of compassion

(तस्य) - its

च - and

प्रसादात् - through divine favour

सुलभा - that which is easily achievable

कृपा - grace

ब्रह्मभावात् - by attaining oneness with Akṣarabrahman

हि - indeed

प्रसीदेत् - is pleased

The entity of Akṣara-Puruṣottama, attainable through grace, is deeply compassionate. If one earns Akṣara-Puruṣottama's divine favour, its grace becomes easily achievable. Such divine favour is earned by achieving oneness with Akṣarabrahman. (143)

तस्माद्धि ब्रह्मभावोऽयं सम्यगिह निरूप्यते।
सर्वसाधनराशिस्तु यस्मिन्नन्तर्गतः सदा॥ १४४॥

tasmāddhi brahmabhāvo'yaṃ samyagiha nirūpyate,
sarvasādhanarāśistu yasminnantargataḥ sadā.

पदच्छेदः - तस्मात्, हि, ब्रह्मभावः, अयम्, सम्यक्, इह, निरूप्यते, सर्वसाधनराशिः, तु, यस्मिन्, अन्तर्गतः, सदा॥

अन्वयः

तस्मात् - therefore

हि - certainly

इह - here

अयम् - this

ब्रह्मभावः - the disposition of being one with Akṣarabrahman

सम्यग् - completely

निरूप्यते - is explained

यस्मिन् - within which

तु - indeed

सर्वसाधनराशिः - all spiritual endeavours

सदा - always

अन्तर्गतः - are encompassed

Therefore, the principle of attaining oneness with Akṣarabrahman is thoroughly explained here. Indeed, all spiritual endeavours are forever encompassed within this practice. (144)

ब्रह्मगुणसमावाप्तिर्भक्तये परब्रह्मणः।
ब्रह्मप्रसंगजा दिव्या कीर्तिता ब्रह्मरूपता॥ १४५॥

brahmaguṇasamāvāptirbhaktaye parabrahmaṇaḥ,
brahmaprasaṃgajā divyā kīrtitā brahmarūpatā.

पदच्छेदः - ब्रह्मगुणसमावाप्तिः, भक्तये, परब्रह्मणः, ब्रह्मप्रसंगजा, दिव्या, कीर्तिता, ब्रह्मरूपता॥

अन्वयः

परब्रह्मणः भक्तये - for the worship of Parabrahman

ब्रह्मगुणसमावाप्तिः - the attainment of Akṣarabrahman's qualities

(आवश्यकी) - is required

ब्रह्मप्रसंगजा - that which arises through profound association with the Akṣarabrahman guru

(इयं) दिव्या (स्थितिः) - this divine state

ब्रह्मरूपता - the state of being brahmarūpa

(इति) - the aforesaid

कीर्तिता - is described as

The attainment of Akṣarabrahman's qualities is essential for worshipping Parabrahman. This divine spiritual state, which arises through profound association with the Akṣarabrahman guru, is also described as the state of being brahmarūpa. (145)

Becoming brahmarūpa has thus been defined as attaining oneness with Akṣarabrahman. The author now elaborates on what such oneness implies.

गुरोर्ज्ञानमिव ज्ञानं वर्तनमपि तत्समम्।
देहार्पणं तथा भक्तौ ब्रह्मात्मैक्यं तदुच्यते॥ १४६ ॥

gurorjñānamiva jñānaṃ vartanamapi tatsamam,
dehārpaṇaṃ tathā bhaktau brahmātmaikyaṃ taducyate.

पदच्छेदः - गुरोः, ज्ञानम्, इव, ज्ञानम्, वर्तनम्, अपि, तत्समम्, देहार्पणम्, तथा, भक्तौ, ब्रह्मात्मैक्यम्, तत्, उच्यते॥

अन्वयः

गुरोः - the guru's

ज्ञानम् - understanding

इव - like

ज्ञानम् - understanding

वर्तनम् - behaviour

अपि - also

तत्समम् - like the guru

तथा - and

भक्तौ - in worship

देहार्पणम् - dedicating one's physical being

तत् - this

ब्रह्मात्मैक्यम् - the ātman's oneness with Akṣarabrahman

उच्यते - is said to be

Becoming one with Akṣarabrahman means having an understanding like that of the Akṣarabrahman guru, behaving virtuously like the guru, and dedicating one's physical being towards bhakti, again, just as the guru has done. (146)

परब्रह्मणि भक्तिं तु ब्रह्मभावोऽप्यपेक्षते।
किमपि साधनं भक्तिं विना नैव प्रसिध्यति॥ १४७॥

parabrahmaṇi bhaktiṃ tu brahmabhāvo'pyapekṣate,
kimapi sādhanaṃ bhaktiṃ vinā naiva prasidhyati.

पदच्छेदः - परब्रह्मणि, भक्तिम्, तु, ब्रह्मभावः, अपि, अपेक्षते, किम्, अपि, साधनम्, भक्तिम्, विना, न, एव, प्रसिध्यति॥

अन्वयः

ब्रह्मभावः - brahmabhāva

अपि - even

परब्रह्मणि - towards Parabrahman

भक्तिम् - bhakti

तु - certainly

अपेक्षते - requires

(यतः) - because

किम् अपि साधनम् - no spiritual endeavour

भक्तिम् - bhakti

विना - without

न एव - cannot indeed

प्रसिध्यति - come to fruition

The state of brahmabhāva undoubtedly entails the worship of Parabrahman, as no spiritual endeavour can be accomplished without bhakti. (147)

8.4 Ekāntika Dharma

Encompassed within this Brāhmic state is ekāntika dharma, a collective name for the four spiritual endeavours of dharma, jñāna, vairāgya, and bhakti. The most significant amongst these endeavours is bhakti, which attains maturity in the presence of its counterparts.

धर्मो ज्ञानं च वैराग्यं भक्तिश्चैतैस्त्रिभिर्युता।
ज्ञेय एकान्तिको धर्मः प्रभुप्रसादसाधनम्॥ १४८॥

dharmo jñānaṃ ca vairāgyaṃ bhaktiścaitaistribhiryutā,
jñeya ekāntiko dharmaḥ prabhuprasādasādhanam.

पदच्छेदः - धर्मः, ज्ञानम्, च, वैराग्यम्, भक्तिः, च, एतैः, त्रिभिः, युता, ज्ञेयः, एकान्तिकः, धर्मः, प्रभुप्रसादसाधनम्॥

अन्वयः

धर्मः - dharma

ज्ञानम् - jñān (wisdom)

वैराग्यं च - and vairāgya (detachment)

एतैः - these

त्रिभिः - three

युता - accompanied by

भक्तिः - bhakti

च - and

एकान्तिकः - ekāntika

धर्मः - dharma

ज्ञेयः - should be known as

(अयं धर्मः) - this dharma

प्रभुप्रसादसाधनम् - the means to attain Paramātman's grace

(अस्ति) - is

Bhakti that is accompanied by dharma, jñāna, and vairāgya should be known as ekāntika dharma. This ekāntika dharma is the means to attaining Paramātman's grace. (148)

अयं भागवतो धर्मः सम्बन्धादुच्यते हरेः।
यस्य संस्थापनार्थाय सम्भवस्तु हरेरिह॥ १४९॥

ayaṃ bhāgavato dharmaḥ sambandhāducyate hareḥ,
yasya saṃsthāpanārthāya sambhavastu hareriha.

पदच्छेदः - अयम्, भागवतः, धर्मः, सम्बन्धात्, उच्यते, हरेः, यस्य, संस्थापनार्थाय, सम्भवः, तु, हरेः, इह॥

अन्वयः

अयम् - this (ekāntika dharma)

हरेः सम्बन्धात् - because of its association with Paramātman

भागवतः - bhāgavata

धर्मः - dharma

(इति) - the aforementioned

उच्यते - is called

यस्य - of that which

संस्थापनार्थाय - for the establishment

तु - indeed

हरेः - Paramātman's

इह - here

सम्भवः - incarnation

Ekāntika dharma is also called bhāgavata dharma because of its association with Paramātman.[59] Paramātman incarnates on earth to establish this sacred dharma.[60] (149)

59 The Saṃskṛta term 'bhagavān' often refers to Paramātman. Here, its nominal base, 'bhagavat', has been derived through the use of a suffix to read 'bhāgavata', which means 'that which is related to Paramātman'. (Pāṇini Sūtra 4.3.120, 4.1.83; Govindācārya 186, 147).

60 See Bhadreshdas' pivotal interpretations of the renowned *Bhagavadgīta* verses, 'svalpamapyasya dharmasya trāyate mahato bhayāt' (2.40) and 'yadā yadā hi dharmasya glānirbhavati bhārata' (4.7-8) in the *Bhagavadgītā-svāminārāyaṇa-bhāṣyam* (p.42-50, 95-6).

अस्माद्धि सुतरां न्यूना धर्मा वर्णाऽऽश्रमोचिताः ।
केवला भक्तिहीनाश्च भगवद्योगवर्जिताः ॥ १५० ॥

asmāddhi sutarāṃ nyūnā dharmā varṇā''śramocitāḥ,
kevalā bhaktihīnāśca bhagavadyogavarjitāḥ.

पदच्छेदः - अस्मात्, हि, सुतराम्, न्यूनाः, धर्माः, वर्णाऽऽश्रमोचिताः, केवलाः, भक्तिहीनाः, च, भगवद्योगवर्जिताः ॥

अन्वयः

अस्माद् (भागवतधर्मात्) - than this bhāgavata dharma

भगवद्योगवर्जिताः - that which lacks the association of Paramātman

भक्तिहीनाः च - and that which lacks bhakti

केवलाः - only

वर्णाऽऽश्रमोचिताः - that which is in accordance with varṇa and āśrama

धर्माः - dharmas

हि - certainly

सुतराम् - extremely

न्यूनाः - insignificant

The dharma of varṇa and āśrama, when it lacks association with Paramātman and is deficient of bhakti, is exceptionally insignificant in comparison to this bhāgavata dharma. (150)

भक्तेरेवेह प्राधान्यं धर्मादिकचतुष्टये।
भक्तेरङ्गतयैवैषां साधनत्वप्रबोधनात्॥ १५१ ॥

bhaktereveha prādhānyaṃ dharmādikacatuṣṭaye,
bhakteraṅgatayaivaiṣāṃ sādhanatvaprabodhanāt.

पदच्छेदः - भक्तेः, एव, इह, प्राधान्यम्, धर्मादिकचतुष्टये, भक्तेः, अङ्गतया, एव, एषाम्, साधनत्वप्रबोधनात्॥

अन्वयः

इह - here

धर्मादिकचतुष्टये - amongst dharma and the other virtues that make up the group of four [elements of ekāntika dharma]

भक्तेः - bhakti's

एव - alone

प्राधान्यम् - predominance

(प्रवर्तते) - prevails

एषाम् - of these

भक्तेः - bhakti's

अङ्गतया - in reference to their position as being supplementary

एव - indeed

साधनत्वप्रबोधनात् - because they are described as tools

Bhakti alone is paramount amongst the four components of ekāntika dharma. This is said because the other three (dharma, jñāna, and vairāgya) are described as tools that are supplementary to bhakti. (151)

8.5 Dharma

The author now elucidates the four components of ekāntika dharma, starting with dharma. He explains that dharma means following God's and the guru's ordinances, which is an endeavour that is open to people of all varṇas and āśramas.

आज्ञा हरेर्गुरोश्चैव सदाचारादिरूपिणी।
शास्त्राऽऽदेशाऽऽत्मको धर्मो विधिनिषेधलक्षणः ॥ १५२ ॥

ājñā harerguroścaiva sadācārādirūpiṇī,
śāstrā''deśā''tmako dharmo vidhiniṣedhalakṣaṇaḥ.

पदच्छेदः - आज्ञा, हरेः, गुरोः, च, एव, सदाचारादिरूपिणी, शास्त्राऽऽदेशात्मकः, धर्मः, विधिनिषेधलक्षणः ॥

अन्वयः

हरेः - Paramātman's

गुरोः च - and the guru's

सदाचारादिरूपिणी - in the form of moral living

आज्ञा - ordinance

(तथा) - and

शास्त्रादेशाऽऽत्मकः - in the form of scriptural injunctions

विधिनिषेधलक्षणः - characterised by guidelines for what to do and what not to do

एव - alone

धर्मः - dharma

(अस्ति) - is

Dharma is defined as Paramātman's and the Akṣarabrahman guru's ordinance to live morally; it also entails scriptural injunctions that either promote or negate specific actions (152)

सदाचारादिनिष्ठो यो क्वापि वर्णस्थितो भवेत्।
स एव साधुर्मन्तव्यः श्रेष्ठश्च धार्मिको बुधैः ॥ १५३ ॥

sadācārādiniṣṭho yo kvāpi varṇasthito bhavet,
sa eva sādhurmantavyaḥ śreṣṭhaśca dhārmiko budhaiḥ.

पदच्छेदः - सदाचारादिनिष्ठः, यः, क्व, अपि, वर्णस्थितः, भवेत्, सः, एव, साधुः, मन्तव्यः, श्रेष्ठः, च, धार्मिकः, बुधैः ॥

अन्वयः

यः - one who

सदाचारादिनिष्ठः - is firmly rooted in moral living and other such practices

क्व अपि - no matter which

वर्णस्थितः भवेत् - varṇa such a person belongs to

सः - this person

एव - alone

बुधैः - by the wise

साधुः - noble

धार्मिकः - righteous

श्रेष्ठः - eminent

च - and

मन्तव्यः - is known

Only one who is firmly rooted in moral living, no matter which varṇa the person belongs to, is recognised by the wise as being noble, righteous, and eminent. (153)

The verse mentioned above is illustrated using a well-known example from the Swaminarayan fellowship's history:

सगरामादयः श्रेष्ठा साधवो धार्मिका मताः ।
ब्राह्मणवच्च पूज्यास्ते जात्या शूद्रा हि यद्यपि ॥ १५४ ॥

sagarāmādayaḥ śreṣṭhā sādhavo dhārmikā matāḥ,
brāhmaṇavacca pūjyāste jātyā śūdrā hi yadyapi.

पदच्छेदः - सगरामादयः, श्रेष्ठाः, साधवः, धार्मिकाः, मताः, ब्राह्मणवत्, च, पूज्याः, ते, जात्या, शूद्राः, हि, यद्यपि ॥

अन्वयः

सगरामादयः (भक्ताः) - Sagarāma and other devotees

श्रेष्ठाः - eminent

साधवः - noble

धार्मिकाः - righteous

च - and

मताः - were known as

ते - they

यद्यपि - although

जात्या - by caste

शूद्राः - śūdra

(तथापि) - yet still

ब्राह्मणवत् - like Brāhmaṇas

हि - indeed

पूज्याः - were worthy of being venerated

Devotees like Sagrāma and others were known as eminent, noble, and righteous. Though born as Śūdras, they were worthy of being venerated as Brāhmaṇas.[61] (154)

61 Sagrāma was a man who lived in the village of Limli. He came from a community that was considered to be low by the people of the time. Nonetheless, he was a faithful devotee who adhered to lofty ideals such as honesty, chastity, and purity. His righeous conduct had earned him great respect. Bhadreshdas notes in this verse that many such devotees were widely respected in the sampradāya. (Dave, *Bhagavān Śrī Svāminārāyaṇa*, Vol.5, 300). He further elaborates in the *Svāminārāyaṇa-siddhānta-sudhā* by stating that spirituality

8.6 Jñāna

The author now explains jñāna, the second facet of ekāntika dharma.

अहमात्माऽस्म्यहं ब्रह्म ब्रह्मरूपे मयि प्रभुः।
इति साक्षाद् ब्रह्मयोगाद् यो भावः साऽऽत्मरूपता॥ १५५॥

ahamātmā'smyahaṃ brahma brahmarūpe mayi prabhuḥ,
iti sākṣād brahmayogād yo bhāvaḥ sā''tmarūpatā.

पदच्छेदः - अहम्, आत्मा, अस्मि, अहम्, ब्रह्म, ब्रह्मरूपे, मयि, प्रभुः, इति, साक्षात्, ब्रह्मयोगात्, यः, भावः, सा, आत्मरूपता॥

अन्वयः

अहम् - I

आत्मा - the ātman

अस्मि - am

अहम् - I

ब्रह्म - Akṣarabrahman

(अस्मि) - am

ब्रह्मरूपे मयि (आत्मनि) - in my brahmarūpa ātman

प्रभुः - Paramātman

(अस्ति) - resides

इति - such

यः - that which

भावः - belief

साक्षाद् ब्रह्मयोगाद् - through direct association with Akṣarabrahman

सा - this

आत्मरूपता - the state of being ātmarūpa

(उच्यते) - is called

The state of being ātmarūpa means believing, through direct association with the brahmasvarūpa guru, 'I am the ātman', 'I am Akṣarabrahman', and 'Parabrahman resides in my brahmarūpa ātman'. (155)

---

is not restricted to people of a certain caste. Instead, he says that spiritual perfection is an achievement that is open to all (Bhadreshdas 335-36). He expresses similar sentiments in the *Brahmasūtra-svāminārāyaṇa-bhāṣyam's* 'śugadhikaraṇa' (Bhadreshdas 120-21).

8.7 Vairāgya

The author then defines vairāgya, ekāntika dharma's third component.

ब्रह्मपरात्मभिन्नेषु रागाभावो विरागता।
ज्ञानांऽशसहिता नित्यं भक्त्युपकारिणी भवेत्॥ १५६॥

brahmaparātmabhinneṣu rāgābhāvo virāgatā,
jñānāṃ'śasahitā nityaṃ bhaktyupakāriṇī bhavet.

पदच्छेदः - ब्रह्मपरात्मभिन्नेषु, रागाभावः, विरागता, ज्ञानांऽशसहिता, नित्यम्, भक्त्युपकारिणी, भवेत्॥

अन्वयः

विरागता - vairāgya

(नाम) - means

ब्रह्मपरात्मभिन्नेषु - in anything other than Akṣarabrahman and Parabrahman

रागाभावः - dispassion

(सा अपि) - that also

नित्यम् - perennially

ज्ञानांशसहिता - with spiritual wisdom

(स्यात्) - if it is

(तदा एव) - then only

भक्त्युपकारिणी - supplemental to bhakti

भवेत् - is

Dispassion towards all except for Akṣarabrahman and Parabrahman is vairāgya. However, such vairāgya only supplements bhakti if it is perennially equipped with spiritual wisdom. (156)

8.8 Bhakti

Now, the author elaborates on bhakti, the final and most essential component of ekāntika dharma.

भक्तिस्तु सहजानन्दे माहात्म्यज्ञानभूषिता।
दिव्याऽनन्या परा प्रीतिर्लौकिकभाववर्जिता॥ १५७॥

bhaktistu sahajānande māhātmyajñānabhūṣitā,
divyā'nanyā parā prītirlaukikabhāvavarjitā.

भक्तिः, तु, सहजानन्दे, माहात्म्यज्ञानभूषिता, दिव्या, अनन्या, परा, प्रीतिः, लौकिकभाववर्जिता॥

अन्वयः

सहजानन्दे - for Sahajanand (Swaminarayan)

माहात्म्यज्ञानभूषिता - ornamented with an understanding of [his] greatness.

लौकिकभाववर्जिता - free of worldly sentiments

दिव्या - characterised by divinity

अनन्या - singular

परा - extreme

प्रीतिः - love

तु - indeed

भक्तिः - bhakti

(उच्यते) - is called

Bhakti is known as extreme, singular love for Sahajanand (Swaminarayan) that is accompanied by an understanding of his greatness, characterised by divinity, and devoid of worldly sentiments. (157)

भक्तिर्नानाविधा प्रोक्ता श्रवणकीर्तनादिका।
भक्ताऽभिरुचिभेदाद्धि तत्र वैविध्यदर्शनम्॥ १५८॥

bhaktirnānāvidhā proktā śravaṇakīrtanādikā,
bhaktā'bhirucibhedāddhi tatra vaividhyadarśanam.

<u>पदच्छेदः</u> - भक्तिः, नानाविधा, प्रोक्ता, श्रवणकीर्तनादिका, भक्ताऽभिरुचिभेदात्, हि, तत्र, वैविध्यदर्शनम्॥

<u>अन्वयः</u>

भक्तिः - bhakti

श्रवणकीर्तनादिका - śravaṇa, kīrtana, etc.

नानाविधा - of many types

प्रोक्ता - has been described

तत्र - there (in the subject of bhakti)

भक्ताऽभिरुचिभेदाद् - due to devotees' varying inclinations

हि - indeed

वैविध्यदर्शनम् - the seeing of variety

(वर्तते) - occurs

Bhakti has been described as being of many types, such as śravaṇa and kīrtana. Such variety occurs due to devotees' varying inclinations. (158)

Bhakti should be offered with an understanding of Paramātman's greatness. Here, the author defines such understanding as upāsanā. He then argues that such bhakti should be offered to Paramātman's manifest form, which presides amongst us through the Akṣarabrahman guru.

सर्वकर्ता समुत्कृष्टः साकृतिः प्रकटः सदा।
इत्यादिगुरुलब्धा धीर्ज्ञेया हरेरुपासना॥ १५९॥

sarvakartā samutkṛṣṭaḥ sākṛtiḥ prakaṭaḥ sadā,
ityādigurulabdhā dhīrjñeyā harerupāsanā.

पदच्छेदः - सर्वकर्ता, समुत्कृष्टः, साकृतिः, प्रकटः, सदा, इत्यादिगुरुलब्धा, धीः, ज्ञेया, हरेः, उपासना॥

अन्वयः

(परमात्मा) - Paramātman

सर्वकर्ता - the omniagent

समुत्कृष्टः - that which is superior to all

सदा - eternally

साकृतिः - that which has form

प्रकटः (च) - and that which is manifest

इत्यादिगुरुलब्धा धीः - this and other such understanding attained from the Akṣarabrahman guru

हरेः - Paramātman's

उपासना - upāsanā

ज्ञेया - should be known as

Paramātman is the omniagent, is superior to all, forever possesses a distinct form, and is eternally manifest. This and other such understanding, acquired from the Akṣarabrahman guru, is to be known as upāsanā. (159)

प्रत्यक्षभक्तिरेवोक्ता श्रेष्ठा कृत्स्नफलप्रदा।
नारायणस्वरूपेऽतो गुरुहरौ विधीयते॥ १६०॥

pratyakṣabhaktirevoktā śreṣṭhā kṛtsnaphalapradā,
nārāyaṇasvarūpe'to guruharau vidhīyate.

पदच्छेदः - प्रत्यक्षभक्तिः, एव, उक्ता, श्रेष्ठा, कृत्स्नफलप्रदा, नारायणस्वरूपे, अतः, गुरुहरौ, विधीयते॥

अन्वयः

प्रत्यक्षभक्तिः - manifest bhakti (bhakti towards God's manifest form)

एव - alone

श्रेष्ठा - the greatest [form of devotion]

कृत्स्नफलप्रदा (च) - and the giver of all fruits

उक्ता - is said to be

अतः - therefore

नारायणस्वरूपे गुरुहरौ - towards the guru-hari, who is the form of Nārāyaṇa

(इयं भक्तिः) - such bhakti

विधीयते - is offered

Bhakti towards God's manifest form alone is the greatest form of devotion and it alone is said to bear all fruits. Therefore, such bhakti is offered to the guru-hari,[62] who is the form of Nārāyaṇa. (160)

62 Swaminarayan uses the term 'guru-hari' to describe the Akṣarabrahman guru, through whom God manifests, in Vacanāmṛta GA-2 (Swaminarayan 545-57). The use of this term to describe the guru explicitly states the principle being described in this verse – namely, that the guru embodies God and is thus God's manifest form.

8.9 Spiritual Endeavour

The author summarises the Akṣara-Puruṣottama Darśana's key spiritual practices over the next two verses and proclaims that one can perfect these practices through association with the Akṣarabrahman guru. The two verses thereafter summarise the words used in the Vacanāmṛta to describe the importance of the Akṣarabrahman guru in order to master the endeavours mentioned here.

इन्द्रियसंयमो मायाविकारादिविदारणम् ।
एकान्तधर्मपुष्टिश्च स्वात्मनि ब्रह्मरूपता ॥ १६१ ॥

indriyasaṃyamo māyāvikārādividāraṇam,
ekāntadharmapuṣṭiśca svātmani brahmarūpatā.

पदच्छेदः - इन्द्रियसंयमः, मायाविकारादिविदारणम्, एकान्तधर्मपुष्टिः, च, स्वात्मनि, ब्रह्मरूपता ॥

अन्वयः

इन्द्रियसंयमः - self-control

मायाविकारादिविदारणम् - the eradication of māyic flaws

एकान्तधर्मपुष्टिः - the nourishment of ekāntika dharma.

स्वात्मनि - in one's ātman

ब्रह्मरूपता - the brahmarūpa state

Control over the senses, the eradication of flaws arising from māyā, the nourishment of ekāntika dharma, and the realisation of one's ātman as brahmarūpa; (161)

माहात्म्यसहितः सम्यङ्निश्चयः परमात्मनः।
मोक्षः सर्वार्थसिद्धिर्हि प्रत्यक्षब्रह्मसङ्गतः॥ १६२॥

māhātmyasahitaḥ samyaṅniścayaḥ paramātmanaḥ,
mokṣaḥ sarvārthasiddhirhi pratyakṣabrahmasaṅgataḥ.

पदच्छेदः - माहात्म्यसहितः, सम्यक्, निश्चयः, परमात्मनः, मोक्षः, सर्वार्थसिद्धिः, हि, प्रत्यक्षब्रह्मसङ्गतः॥

अन्वयः

माहात्म्यसहितः - with knowledge of [Paramātman's] glory

परमात्मनः - Paramātman's

सम्यक् - complete

निश्चयः - conviction

मोक्षः - liberation

सर्वार्थसिद्धिः च - and the achievement of all else that is to be achieved

हि (प्राप्यते) - is certainly attained

प्रत्यक्षब्रह्मसङ्गतः - through the association of the Akṣarabrahman guru

Liberation, complete conviction in God that is characterised by the knowledge of God's glory, and all else that is to be achieved is attained through association with the manifest, Akṣarabrahman guru. (162)

परमैकान्तिको भक्तः साधुः सत्पुरुषश्च सन्।
एकान्तिको गुरुः साक्षाद् महापुरुष आदिभिः ॥ १६३ ॥
एकमेवाक्षरं ब्रह्म मोक्षोपायतया ध्रुवम्।
वचनामृतवाक्येषु नानाशब्दैः प्रदर्शितम् ॥ १६४ ॥

paramaikāntiko bhaktaḥ sādhuḥ satpuruṣaśca san,
ekāntiko guruḥ sākṣād mahāpuruṣa ādibhiḥ.
ekamevākṣaraṃ brahma mokṣopāyatayā dhruvam,
vacanāmṛtavākyeṣu nānāśabdaiḥ pradarśitam.

पदच्छेदः - परमैकान्तिकः, भक्तः, साधुः, सत्पुरुषः, च, सन्, एकान्तिकः, गुरुः, साक्षात्, महापुरुषः, आदिभिः, एकम्, एव, अक्षरम्, ब्रह्म, मोक्षोपायतया, ध्रुवम्, वचनामृतवाक्येषु, नानाशब्दैः, प्रदर्शितम् ॥

अन्वयः

वचनामृतवाक्येषु - in the Vacanāmṛta's teachings
एकम् एव - the one and only
अक्षरं ब्रह्म - Akṣarabrahman
परमैकान्तिकः - param ekāntika
भक्तः - bhakta
साधुः - sādhu
सत्पुरुषः - satpuruṣa
सन् - sant
एकान्तिकः - ekāntika
गुरुः - guru
साक्षात् - manifest
महापुरुषः - mahāpuruṣa
च - and
आदिभिः नानाशब्दैः - through these and other terms
मोक्षोपायतया - as the key to liberation
ध्रुवम् - invariably
प्रदर्शितम् - has been shown

In the Vacanāmṛta, the one and only Akṣarabrahman is referred to as the param ekāntika bhakta, sādhu, satpuruṣa, sant, ekāntika, guru, and the manifest mahāpuruṣa. Through these and other such terms, Akṣarabrahman invariably has been shown as the key to liberation. (163-4)

The author concludes with three verses that enumerate specific spiritual endeavours, foremost of which is attaining oneness with Akṣarabrahman.

उत्साहोऽभ्यसनं धैर्यं विश्वासः संयमो बलम्।
सुहृद्भावस्तथैक्यं च दासत्वं गुरुसेवनम्॥ १६५॥

utsāho'bhyasanaṃ dhairyaṃ viśvāsaḥ saṃyamo balam,
suhṛdbhāvastathaikyaṃ ca dāsatvaṃ gurusevanam.

पदच्छेदः - उत्साहः, अभ्यसनम्, धैर्यम्, विश्वासः, संयमः, बलम्, सुहृद्भावः, तथा, ऐक्यम्, च, दासत्वम्, गुरुसेवनम्॥

अन्वयः

उत्साहः - enthusiasm

अभ्यसनम् - repeated practice [of spiritual endeavours]

धैर्यम् - forbearance

विश्वासः - faith

संयमः - self-control

बलम् - strength

सुहृद्भावः - fraternity

ऐक्यम् - unity

दासत्वम् - humility

तथा च - and

गुरुसेवनम् - service towards the Akṣarabrahman guru

Enthusiasm, repeated practice of spiritual endeavours, forbearance, faith, self-control, strength, fraternity, unity, humility, and service towards the Akṣarabrahman guru; (165)

प्रार्थना च मुमुक्षा च सहश्च गुणग्राहिता।
प्राप्त्यादिकाऽनुसन्धानमन्तर्दृष्टिस्तथाऽऽह्निकम्॥ १६६ ॥

prārthanā ca mumukṣā ca sahaśca guṇagrāhitā,
prāptyādikā'nusandhānamantardṛṣṭis-tathā''hnikam.

पदच्छेदः - प्रार्थना, च, मुमुक्षा, च, सहः, च, गुणग्राहिता, प्राप्त्यादिकाऽनुसन्धानम्, अन्तर्दृष्टिः, तथा, आह्निकम्॥

अन्वयः

प्रार्थना - prayer

च - and

मुमुक्षा - a desire for liberation

सहः - tolerance

गुणग्राहिता - appreciation of the good in others

प्राप्त्यादिकाऽनुसन्धानम् - awareness of such concepts as the significance and glory of that which we have attained [in the form of satsaṅga]

अन्तर्दृष्टिः - introspection

तथा च - as well as

आह्निकम् च - and daily offerings of bhakti

Prayer, a desire for liberation, tolerance, appreciation of the good in others, awareness of such concepts as the significance and glory of satsaṅga, introspection, and daily offerings of bhakti; (166)

एतानि साधनानि स्युर्गुरुप्रसन्नता यतः।
साक्षाद् ब्रह्मप्रसङ्गस्तु तेष्वपि प्रमुखं भवेत्॥ १६७॥

etāni sādhanāni syurguruprasannatā yataḥ,
sākṣād brahmaprasaṅgastu teṣvapi pramukhaṃ bhavet.

पदच्छेदः - एतानि, साधनानि, स्युः, गुरुप्रसन्नता, यतः, साक्षात्, ब्रह्मप्रसङ्गः, तु, तेषु, अपि, प्रमुखम्, भवेत्॥

अन्वयः

एतानि - these
साधनानि - spiritual endeavours
स्युः - are
यतः - through which
गुरुप्रसन्नता - the guru's grace
(प्राप्यते) - is earned
तेषु (साधनेषु) - amongst these endeavours
अपि - indeed
साक्षाद् - itself
ब्रह्मप्रसङ्गः - association with the Akṣarabrahman guru
तु - truly
प्रमुखम् - foremost
(साधनम्) - endeavour
भवेत् - is

These are spiritual endeavours through which one earns the guru's grace. However, amongst all of these, association with the Akṣarabrahman guru is truly the foremost endeavour. (167)

एवं परब्रह्मस्वामिनारायणप्रबोधित-ब्रह्मस्वरूपगुणातीतगुरुपरम्परोपबृंहित-
ब्रह्मविद्यालक्षणाऽक्षरपुरुषोत्तमदर्शनप्रतिपादके
साधुभद्रेशदासविरचिते
स्वामिनारायणसिद्धान्तसुधाऽऽख्ये शास्त्रेऽस्मिन्
समाप्तं साधनधारा
नामऽष्टमं प्रकरणम् ॥

In this way ends the eighth chapter, known as the 'Sādhana-dhārā', of Sadhu Bhadreshdas' *Svāminārāyaṇa-siddhānta-sudhā*, a text that substantiates the Akṣara-Puruṣottama Darśana, which is characterised as brahmavidyā, was taught by Parabrahman Swaminarayan, and has been fostered by the lineage of brahmasvarūpa, guṇātīta gurus.

Chapter 9

Phala-dhārā

9.1 Introduction

The *Svāminārāyaṇa-siddhānta-sudhā*'s final chapter discusses liberation, the ultimate fruit of spiritual endeavour. The author defines liberation as a state in which one has attained oneness with Akṣarabrahman and offers bhakti to Parabrahman. He further explains two types of liberation, or mukti – jivan-mukti and videha-mukti. Jivan-mukti is spiritual perfection that is achieved while one is still living, while videha-mukti is the state a liberated being experiences after death.

This chapter explains videha-mukti at length, describing the process by which one becomes a videha-mukta and the benefits that the videha-mukta enjoys. Specifically, it says that Akṣara and Puruṣottama take the released being to Akṣaradhāman, Paramātman's divine abode, after the death of the physical body. In the state of videha-mukti, the released being receives a new body, known as a brāhmī tanu, and enjoys eternal bliss.

The author concludes his work by contextualising it in terms of the Akṣara-Puruṣottama Darśana at large. He recounts the darśana's five primary sources of knowledge – the Vacanāmṛta, the Svāmīnī Vāto, the texts recounting the lives of the Akṣarabrahman gurus, Pramukh Swami Maharaj's 'Siddhānta-patram', and direct association with the manifest, brahmasvarūpa guru. He also praises the countless people that live the Akṣara-Puruṣottama Darśana, describing their imbibing of the tradition as being far above mere scriptural enquiry. He ends by again praising association with the brahmasvarūpa guru and praying that he may be forever blessed with such association.

9.2 Benediction

यत्कारुण्यकणस्पर्शान्मुक्तिः करतलायते।
नारायणस्वरूपाय नमोऽस्तु भद्रकाङ्क्षया॥ १६८॥

yatkāruṇyakaṇasparśānmuktiḥ karatalāyate,
nārāyaṇasvarūpāya namo'stu bhadrakāṅkṣayā.

पदच्छेदः - यत्कारुण्यकणस्पर्शात्, मुक्तिः, करतलायते, नारायणस्वरूपाय, नमोऽस्तु भद्रकाङ्क्षया ॥

अन्वयः

मुक्तिः - liberation

यत्कारुण्यकणस्पर्शात् - by the touch of even of a grain of whose compassion

करतलायते - is made to rest in the palm of one's hand

भद्रकाङ्क्षया - with auspicious thoughts

नारायणस्वरूपाय - to Narayanswaroop

नमः - homage

अस्तु - may there be

With auspicious intentions, I offer homage to Narayanswaroop. Indeed, by the touch of even a grain of his compassion, liberation is easily attained, as if it rests in the palm of one's hand. (168)

9.3 Defining Liberation

मुक्तिर्हि स्वात्मब्रह्मैक्यपूर्वकं दासभावतः।
भजनोपासनं प्रीत्या स्वामिनारायणप्रभोः॥ १६९॥

muktirhi svātmabrahmaikya-pūrvakaṃ dāsabhāvataḥ,
bhajanopāsanaṃ prītyā svāminārāyaṇaprabhoḥ.

पदच्छेदः - मुक्तिः, हि, स्वात्मब्रह्मैक्यपूर्वकम्, दासभावतः, भजनोपासनम्, प्रीत्या, स्वामिनारायणप्रभोः॥

अन्वयः

स्वात्मब्रह्मैक्यपूर्वकम् - characterised by the qualitative oneness of one's ātman with Akṣarabrahman

स्वामिनारायणप्रभोः - Bhagwan Swaminarayan's

दासभावतः - with humility

प्रीत्या - with love

भजनोपासनम् - worship

हि - indeed

मुक्तिः - mukti (liberation)

(कथ्यते) - is called

Mukti (liberation) is humbly and lovingly worshipping Bhagwan Swaminarayan upon having attained qualitative oneness with Akṣarabrahman. (169)

सा पुनर्द्विविधा प्रोक्ता ब्रह्मस्थितिमतां ध्रुवा।
एका जीवत एव स्याद् अन्या च मरणादनु॥ १७०॥

sā punardvividhā proktā brahmasthitimatām dhruvā,
ekā jīvata eva syād anyā ca maraṇādanu.

पदच्छेदः - सा, पुनर्, द्विविधा, प्रोक्ता, ब्रह्मस्थितिमताम्, ध्रुवा, एका, जीवतः, एव, स्यात्, अन्या, च, मरणात्, अनु॥

अन्वयः

ब्रह्मस्थितिमताम् - of those who have attained oneness with Akṣarabrahman

सा - it

ध्रुवा - everlasting

(मुक्तिः) - mukti

पुनः - again

द्विविधा - of two types

प्रोक्ता - said to be

एका - one

जीवत एव - while still living

स्यात् - occurs

अन्या - the other

च - and

मरणादनु - after death

(स्यात्) - occurs

Moreover, this everlasting mukti for those who have attained oneness with Akṣarabrahman is said to be of two types: one that occurs while living and the other after death. (170)

The author explains the concept of the nityamukta, or the eternally liberated being, according to the Akṣara-Puruṣottama Darśana:

द्वावेव नित्यमुक्तौ स्तो ह्यक्षरपुरुषोत्तमौ।
ताभ्यां भिन्नेषु सर्वेषु नाऽनादिमुक्तता मता॥ १७१ ॥

dvāveva nityamuktau sto hyakṣarapuruṣottamau,
tābhyāṃ bhinneṣu sarveṣu nā'nādimuktatā matā.

पदच्छेदः - द्वौ, एव, नित्यमुक्तौ, स्तः, हि, अक्षरपुरुषोत्तमौ, ताभ्याम्, भिन्नेषु, सर्वेषु, न, अनादिमुक्तता, मता॥

अन्वयः

अक्षरपुरुषोत्तमौ - Akṣara and Puruṣottama

हि - indeed

द्वौ - two

एव - only

नित्यमुक्तौ - eternally liberated beings

स्तः - are

ताभ्यां भिन्नेषु सर्वेषु - in all other than these two

अनादिमुक्तता - the state of being eternally liberated

न मता - is not recognised

Akṣara and Puruṣottama are the only two eternally liberated beings. No entity apart from these is recognised to be eternally liberated. (171)

9.4 Videha-mukti

देहपातोत्तरं लभ्या विदेहमुक्तिरुच्यते।
अक्षरधाम्नि भोग्येयं मूर्तिमद्ब्रह्मणा सह॥ १७२॥

dehapātottaram labhyā videhamuktirucyate,
akṣaradhāmni bhogyeyaṃ mūrtimadbrahmaṇā saha.

पदच्छेदः - देहपातोत्तरम्, लभ्या, विदेहमुक्तिः, उच्यते, अक्षरधाम्नि, भोग्या, इयम्, मूर्तिमद्ब्रह्मणा, सह॥

अन्वयः

देहपातोत्तरम् - after shedding the mortal body

(या) लभ्या - that which is attained

(सा) विदेहमुक्तिः उच्यते - this is known as videha-mukti

इयम् - this

अक्षरधाम्नि - in Akṣaradhāman

मूर्तिमद्ब्रह्मणा सह - with Akṣarabrahman, which appears in a personal form

भोग्या - is experienced

The liberation attained after shedding the mortal body is known as videha-mukti. The released being experiences the bliss of such liberation in Akṣaradhāman along with the personal form of Akṣarabrahman.[63] (172)

63 Taittirīyopaniṣad 2.1.1; Bhadreshdas, *Upaniṣat-svāminārāyaṇa-bhāṣyam*, Vol.1, 361.

प्राप्य नवां तनुं ब्राह्मीं परात्माऽऽकारसंनिभाम्।
नित्यद्विभुजपादादि-दिव्यकरणसंयुताम्॥ १७३॥

prāpya navāṃ tanuṃ brāhmīṃ parātmā''kārasaṃnibhām,
nitya-dvibhuja-pādādi-divyakaraṇa-saṃyutām.

पदच्छेदः - प्राप्य, नवाम्, तनुम्, ब्राह्मीम्, परात्माऽऽकारसंनिभाम्, नित्यद्विभुजपादादि-दिव्यकरणसंयुताम्॥

अन्वयः

(विदेहमुक्तौ) - in the state of videha-mukti

(मुक्तः) - the released being

परात्माऽऽकारसंनिभाम् - that which resembles the form of Paramātman

ब्राह्मीम् - that which is made of the divine element known as Akṣarabrahman

नित्यद्विभुजपादादिदिव्यकरण-संयुताम् - that which eternally possesses two arms, feet, and other divine instruments of action.

नवाम् - new

तनुम् - body

प्राप्य - having attained

(अक्षरधाम्नि) - in Akṣaradhāman

(वसति) - resides

In the state of videha-mukti, the released being attains a new body that is made of the divine element known as Akṣarabrahman. This new body looks just like that of Paramātman and eternally possesses two arms, feet, and other divine instruments of action.[64] (173)

64 See verse 128.

सर्वे मुक्ताः समाऽऽकारा न्यूनाऽधिकत्ववर्जिताः ।
स्त्रीपुरुषत्वशून्याश्च क्षुधादिरहितास्तथा ॥ १७४ ॥

sarve muktāḥ samā''kārā nyūnā'dhikatvavarjitāḥ,
strīpuruṣatvaśūnyāśca kṣudhādirahitāstathā.

पदच्छेदः - सर्वे, मुक्ताः, समाऽऽकाराः, न्यूनाऽधिकत्ववर्जिताः, स्त्रीपुरुषत्वशून्याः, च, क्षुधादिरहिताः, तथा ॥

अन्वयः

(अक्षरधाम्नि) - in Akṣaradhāman

सर्वे - all

मुक्ताः - released beings

समाऽऽकाराः - those who are of similar form

न्यूनाऽधिकत्ववर्जिताः - those who are free of relative insignificance and significance

स्त्रीपुरुषत्वशून्याः - free of differences arising from gender classification

तथा च - and

क्षुधादिरहिताः - free of hunger and other such yearnings

(सन्ति) - are

All of the released beings in Akṣaradhāman possess the same form. There is no difference in their relative significance. They are above gender differences and free of hunger and other such yearnings. (174)

निमग्नाः सहजानन्दे प्रगाढाऽऽनन्दसेविताः ।
कुर्वाणा ब्रह्मभावाऽऽढ्यां तद्भक्तिं दासभावतः ॥ १७५ ॥

nimagnāḥ sahajānande pragāḍhā''nandasevitāḥ,
kurvāṇā brahmabhāvā''ḍhyāṃ tadbhaktiṃ dāsabhāvataḥ.

पदच्छेदः - निमग्नाः, सहजानन्दे, प्रगाढाऽऽनन्दसेविताः, कुर्वाणाः, ब्रह्मभावाऽऽढ्याम्, तद्भक्तिम्, दासभावतः ॥

अन्वयः

(ते मुक्ताः) - those released souls

सहजानन्दे - in Sahajanand

निमग्नाः - those who are immersed

प्रगाढाऽऽनन्दसेविताः - those who enjoy profound bliss

(सन्ति) - are

(तथा च) - and

दासभावतः - with humility

ब्रह्मभावाऽऽढ्याम् - that which is enriched by oneness with Akṣarabrahman

तद्भक्तिम् - his devotion

कुर्वाणाः - those who do

(वर्तन्ते) - are

Immersed in Swaminarayan's divine form, they enjoy profound bliss. They offer humble devotion to him that is enriched by their qualitative oneness with Akṣarabrahman. (175)

भक्तानां ब्रह्मरूपाणामक्षरपुरुषोत्तमौ।
देहपातोत्तरं स्यातां प्रमुखावातिवाहिकौ॥ १७६॥

bhaktānāṃ brahmarūpāṇāmakṣarapuruṣottamau,
dehapātottaraṃ syātāṃ pramukhāvātivāhikau.

पदच्छेदः - भक्तानाम्, ब्रह्मरूपाणाम्, अक्षरपुरुषोत्तमौ, देहपातोत्तरम्, स्याताम्, प्रमुखौ, आतिवाहिकौ॥

अन्वयः

ब्रह्मरूपाणां भक्तानाम् - of devotees who have attained oneness with Akṣarabrahman

देहपातोत्तरम् - after the death of [their mortal] bodies

अक्षरपुरुषोत्तमौ - Akṣara and Puruṣottama

(अक्षरधाम्नः) - Akṣaradhāman's

प्रमुखौ - those who are foremost

आतिवाहिकौ - those who take

स्याताम् - are

Akṣara and Puruṣottama are foremost in taking these brahmarūpa devotees to Akṣaradhāman after these devotees have shed their mortal bodies. (176)

ऐश्वर्यं सर्वमुक्तानां सर्वज्ञत्वादिलक्षणम्।
परप्रसादतो लभ्यं जगद्व्यापारवर्जितम्॥ १७७॥

aiśvaryaṃ sarvamuktānāṃ sarvajñatvādilakṣaṇam,
paraprasādato labhyaṃ jagadvyāpāravarjitam.

पदच्छेदः - ऐश्वर्यम्, सर्वमुक्तानाम्, सर्वज्ञत्वादिलक्षणम्, परप्रसादतः, लभ्यम्, जगद्व्यापारवर्जितम्॥

अन्वयः

परप्रसादतः - by Paramātman's grace

सर्वमुक्तानाम् - of all liberated beings

जगद्व्यापारवर्जितम् - apart from creation

सर्वज्ञत्वादिलक्षणम् (च) - and characterised by omniscience and other qualities

ऐश्वर्यम् - divine faculties

लभ्यम् - attainable

By Paramātman's grace, all liberated beings attain omniscience and other divine faculties. However, the virtues these beings attain do not include the power to engender creation.[65] (177)

---

65 In the classic style of Indian philosophical debate, Bhadreshdas presents five śāstric references in the *Svāminārāyaṇa-siddhānta-sudhā* stating the prima facie view that the released being, indeed, attains the ability engender creation. He defeats this view, however, with an array of passages that show that only Parabrahman initiates creation (p.410-11). He adds in the *Brahmasūtra-svāminārāyaṇa-bhāṣya's* 'jagadvyāpāra adhikaraṇa' (p.427-33) that released souls also cannot liberate others or serve as the divine abode, as these faculties are reserved for Akṣara and Puruṣottama.

पुनरावर्तनं नैव लब्धमुक्तेः कदाचन।
ब्रह्मरूपस्य भक्तस्य परानन्दे निमज्जनम्॥ १७८॥

punarāvartanaṃ naiva labdhamukteḥ kadācana,
brahmarūpasya bhaktasya parānande nimajjanam.

पदच्छेदः - पुनरावर्तनम्, न, एव, लब्धमुक्तेः, कदाचन, ब्रह्मरूपस्य, भक्तस्य, परानन्दे, निमज्जनम्॥

अन्वयः

लब्धमुक्तेः - of one who has attained liberation

कदाचन - at any time

पुनरावर्तनम् - return [to the cycle of transmigration]

न - does not

एव - certainly

(भवति) - occur

ब्रह्मरूपस्य भक्तस्य - the brahmarūpa devotee

परानन्दे - in Paramātman's bliss

निमज्जनम् - immersion

One who has attained liberation never returns to the cycle of transmigration. This brahmarūpa devotee remains immersed in Paramātman's bliss. (178)

9.5 The Significance of these Verses

The author concludes by sharing the purpose of enunciating the essence of the Akṣara-Puruṣottama philosophy through the present verses.

सिद्धान्तसंग्रहेणैवं कारिका रचिता इमाः ।
अभ्यासे मनने पाठे वादे महोपकारिकाः ॥ १७९ ॥

siddhāntasaṃgraheṇaivaṃ kārikā racitā imāḥ,
abhyāse manane pāṭhe vāde mahopakārikāḥ.

पदच्छेदः - सिद्धान्तसंग्रहेण, एवम्, कारिकाः, रचिताः, इमाः, अभ्यासे, मनने, पाठे, वादे, महोपकारिकाः ॥

अन्वयः

इमाः - these

कारिकाः - verses

सिद्धान्तसंग्रहेण - to summarise the [Akṣara-Puruṣottama] principle.

एवम् - in this way

रचिताः - created

(इमाः कारिकाः) - these verses

अभ्यासे - in study

मनने - in reflection

पाठे - in recitation

वादे (च) - and in philosophical discussion

महोपकारिकाः - very useful

(सन्ति) - are

These verses have been created to summarise the Akṣara-Puruṣottama principle. Indeed, these verses facilitate study, reflection, recitation, and philosophical discussion on this doctrine. (179)

एवं परब्रह्मस्वामिनारायणप्रबोधित-ब्रह्मस्वरूपगुणातीतगुरुपरम्परोपबृंहित-
ब्रह्मविद्यालक्षणाऽक्षरपुरुषोत्तमदर्शनप्रतिपादके
साधुभद्रेशदासविरचिते
स्वामिनारायणसिद्धान्तसुधाऽऽख्ये शास्त्रेऽस्मिन्
समाप्तं फलधारा नाम
नवमं प्रकरणम् ॥

In this way ends the ninth chapter, known as the 'Phala-dhārā', of Sadhu Bhadreshdas' *Svāminārāyaṇa-siddhānta-sudhā*, a text that substantiates the Akṣara-Puruṣottama Darśana, which is characterised as brahmavidyā, was taught by Parabrahman Swaminarayan, and has been fostered by the lineage of brahmasvarūpa, guṇātīta gurus.

Concluding Verses & Benediction

The author presents the five nectar-like sources that elaborate upon the Akṣara-Puruṣottama Darśana.

स्वामिवार्ताऽमृतं दिव्यं दिव्यं च वचनाऽमृतम्।
गुरूणां चरितं दिव्यं गुरुलेखाऽमृतं शुभम्॥ १८०॥
गुरुलाभाऽमृतं साक्षाद् हरये गुरवे तथा।
पञ्चाऽमृताऽभिषिक्तोऽहं सुधाऽञ्जलिं समर्पये॥ १८१॥

svāmivārtā'mṛtaṃ divyaṃ divyaṃ ca vacanā'mṛtam,
gurūṇāṃ caritaṃ divyaṃ gurulekhā'mṛtaṃ śubham.

gurulābhā'mṛtaṃ sākṣād haraye gurave tathā,
pañcā'mṛtā'bhiṣikto'haṃ sudhā'ñjaliṃ samarpaye.

पदच्छेदः - स्वामिवार्ताऽमृतम्, दिव्यम्, दिव्यम्, च, वचनाऽमृतम्, गुरूणाम्, चरितम्, दिव्यम्, गुरुलेखाऽमृतम्, शुभम्, गुरुलाभाऽमृतम्, साक्षात्, हरये, गुरवे, तथा, पञ्चाऽमृताऽभिषिक्तः, अहम्, सुधाऽञ्जलिम्, समर्पये॥

अन्वयः

(प्रथमम्) - the first

दिव्यम् - the divine

वचनामृतम् - Vacanāmṛta

(द्वितीयम्) - the second

दिव्यम् - the divine

स्वामिवार्ताऽमृतम् - nectar in the form of the Svāmīnī Vāto

(तृतीयम्) - the third

गुरूणाम् - the Akṣarabrahman gurus'

दिव्यम् - divine

चरितम् - actions

(चतुर्थम्) - the fourth

शुभम् - the auspicious

गुरुलेखामृतम् - nectar in the form of the guru's letter

(पञ्चमम्) - the fifth

च - and

साक्षाद् - direct

गुरुलाभामृतम् - nectar in the form of association with the [living] guru

(एवम्) - in this way

पञ्चामृताऽभिषिक्तः - anointed by the five nectars

अहम् - I

हरये - to Parabrahman

तथा - and

गुरवे - to the guru

सुधाञ्जलिम् - salutations in the form of the [Svāminārāyaṇa Siddhānta] Sudhā

समर्पये - I offer

The first divine nectar is the Vacanāmṛta. The second is the Svāmīnī Vāto. The texts recounting the lives of the Akṣarabrahman gurus are the third. The guru's auspicious letter is the fourth.[66] The fifth is direct association with the living guru. Anointed by these five nectars, I offer my salutations in the form of the *Svāminārāyaṇa-siddhānta-sudhā* to Parabrahman Swaminarayan and my guru. (180-81)

---

66 The guru's letter signifies the 'Siddhānta-patram', a philosophical document written by Pramukh Swami Maharaj (see front matter).

The author ends the text with praises of the guru and the satsaṅga fellowship and, lastly, a prayer.

शब्देषु साधितं यद्धि सप्रपञ्चं निरूपितम्।
नैके तदद्य जीवन्ति गुरुसत्संगवैभवात्॥ १८२॥

śabdeṣu sādhitaṃ yaddhi saprapañcaṃ nirūpitam,
naike tadadya jīvanti gurusatsaṃgavaibhavāt.

पदच्छेदः - शब्देषु, साधितम्, यद्, हि, सप्रपञ्चम्, निरूपितम्, नैके, तत्, अद्य, जीवन्ति, गुरुसत्सङ्गवैभवात्॥

अन्वयः

(अस्मिन् ग्रन्थे) - in this text
यत् - that which
हि - certainly
शब्देषु - in words
साधितम् - has been established
(यत्) - that which
(च) - and
सप्रपञ्चम् - at length
निरूपितम् - has been explained
तत् - that
अद्य - today
गुरुसत्सङ्गवैभवात् - due to the power of association with the Akṣarabrahman guru
नैके - countless
जीवन्ति - live

The principles that have been substantiated and explained at length through words here are lived by countless devotees today due to the power of association with the Akṣarabrahman guru. (182)

सन्तुष्टा दृढनिष्ठातो ह्यक्षरपुरुषोत्तमे।
सत्सङ्गे बहवो दृष्टाः शास्त्रक्लेशविवर्जिताः ॥ १८३ ॥

santuṣṭā dṛḍhaniṣṭhāto hyakṣarapuruṣottame,
satsaṅge bahavo dṛṣṭāḥ śāstrakleśavivarjitāḥ.

पदच्छेदः - सन्तुष्टाः, दृढनिष्ठातः, हि, अक्षरपुरुषोत्तमे, सत्सङ्गे, बहवः, दृष्टाः, शास्त्रक्लेशविवर्जिताः ॥

अन्वयः

अक्षरपुरुषोत्तमे - in Akṣara-Puruṣottama

हि - indeed

दृढनिष्ठातः - due to firm conviction

सन्तुष्टाः - fulfilled

शास्त्रक्लेशविवर्जिताः - without having gone through the pains of scriptural study

बहवः - many

(भक्ताः) - devotees

सत्सङ्गे - in the fellowship

दृष्टाः - can be seen

In the fellowship today, many devotees can be seen who are fulfilled due to their firm conviction in Akṣara-Puruṣottama. These devotees experience this state without having gone through the pains of scriptural study. (183)

सत्सङ्गान्नाधिकं किञ्चिद् गुरुप्रसङ्गलक्षणात्।
एतादृग्ग्रन्थकोटिभ्यः सत्सङ्ग उत्तमस्ततः ॥ १८४ ॥

satsaṅgānnādhikaṃ kiñcid guruprasaṅgalakṣaṇāt,
etādṛggranthakoṭibhyaḥ satsaṅga uttamastataḥ.

पदच्छेदः - सत्सङ्गात्, न, अधिकम्, किञ्चित्, गुरुप्रसङ्गलक्षणात्, एतादृग्ग्रन्थकोटिभ्यः, सत्सङ्गः, उत्तमः, ततः ॥

अन्वयः

गुरुप्रसङ्गलक्षणात् सत्सङ्गाद् - than satsaṅga that is characterised by association with the Akṣarabrahman guru

अधिकम् - greater

किञ्चिद् - anything

नास्ति - is not

ततः - therefore

एतादृग्ग्रन्थकोटिभ्यः - than tens of millions of such texts

सत्सङ्गः - satsaṅga

उत्तमः - is greater

Nothing is superior to satsaṅga that is characterised by association with the Akṣarabrahman guru. Indeed, satsaṅga in this form is even greater than tens of millions of such texts. (184)

श्वासे श्वासे च सत्सङ्गं दिव्यमलौकिकं शुभम्।
पूरयेति गुरो याचे ग्रन्थाऽन्ते भद्रभावतः॥ १८५॥

śvāse śvāse ca satsaṅgaṃ divyamalaukikaṃ śubham,
pūrayeti guro yāce granthā'nte bhadrabhāvataḥ.

पदच्छेदः - श्वासे, श्वासे, च, सत्सङ्गम्, दिव्यम्, अलौकिकम्, शुभम्, पूरय, इति, गुरो, याचे, ग्रन्थाऽन्ते, भद्रभावतः॥

अन्वयः

(हे) गुरो! - O Dear Guru!

(मम) - of mine

श्वासे श्वासे - in every breath

दिव्यम् - divine

अलौकिकम् - extraordinary

शुभम् - blessed

च - and

सत्सङ्गम् - association

पूरय - fill

इति - the aforementioned

ग्रन्थाऽन्ते - at the closing of this text

भद्रभावतः - auspiciously

(अहम्) - I

याचे - ask

O Dear Guru! At the closing of this text, I auspiciously request you to enrich my every breath with your divine, extraordinary, and blessed association. (185)

एवं परब्रह्मस्वामिनारायणप्रबोधित-ब्रह्मस्वरूपगुणातीतगुरुपरम्परोपबृंहित-
ब्रह्मविद्यालक्षणाऽक्षरपुरुषोत्तमदर्शनसंग्राहिका:
साधुभद्रेशदासविरचिता:
स्वामिनारायणसिद्धान्तकारिका:समाप्ता: ॥

In this way ends the *Svāmināṛāyaṇa-siddhānta-kārikās* composed by Sadhu Bhadreshdas, which entail the essence of the Akṣara-Puruṣottama Darśana, which is characterised as brahmavidyā, was taught by Parabrahman Swaminarayan, and has been fostered by the lineage of brahmasvarūpa, guṇātīta gurus.

Appendix

About Mahāmahopādyāya Bhadreshdas Swami
(Author of the *Svāminārāyaṇa-siddhānta-sudhā*)

Bhadreshdas Swami is a renowned Sanskrit scholar born on 12 December 1966, in Maharashtra, India. A disciple of Bhagwan Swaminarayan, he took sannyāsa dikṣā from his spiritual guru, Pramukh Swami Maharaj, in 1981. He has received multiple masters (ācārya) degrees in Sāṃkhya, Yoga, Vedānta, Nyāya, Vaiśeṣika, and the Pūrvamīmāṃsā Darśana. In 2005, he was awarded his doctoral degree for his work on *Paramātmapratyakṣasvarūpayogaḥ*, a comparative analysis of Swaminarayan"s Vacanāmṛta and the *Bhagavadgītā*. Thereafter, he was awarded a D.Litt. from Kavikulguru Kalidas Sanskrit University (KKSU) in 2010 for his contributions to Sanskrit literature, followed by the Mahāmahopādyāya award in 2012 and the Darśanakesarī award in October 2013 from the Akhila Bhāratīya Vidvat Pariṣad.

His magnum opuses are: 1) the *Prasthānatrayī-svāminārāyaṇa-bhāṣyam*, a comprehensive commentary on the ten principle Upaniṣads, the *Bhagavadgītā*, and the *Brahmasūtras*, according to teachings of Bhagavān Svāminārāyaṇa, and 2) the *Svāminārāyaṇa-siddhānta-sudhā*, a didactic treatise that offers a systematic and comprehensive exposition, justification, and defence of the Akṣara-Puruṣottama Darśana's theological and philosophical principles.

Bhadreshdas Swami was a member of the project committee of the Maharshi Sandipani Rashtriya Veda Vidya Pratishthan, Ujjain, an institute governed by India's Ministry of Human Resource Development. He is currently head the BAPS Swaminarayan Research Institute in Delhi, a professor at AARSH (the Akshardham Center for Applied Research in Social Harmony), and a senior advisor for the BAPS Swaminarayan Sanskrit Mahavidyalaya, which is in association with Somnath Sanskrit University,

Veraval, Gujarat.

His current projects include surveying Indological research throughout the world. He has visited more than 81 universities in 18 countries and has engaged in conversation regarding current research in Sanskrit linguistics and history, Indian philosophy and epistemology, Vedic literature, the Prasthānatrayī, comparative studies of religion, and the philosophy of religion.

Index of Verses

The *Svāminārāyaṇa-siddhānta-sudhā* consists of a total of 548 verses. Of these, 458 have been earmarked as kārikās, or verses that summarise the text's core teachings and are explained at length in the *Siddhanta-sudhā's* prose. The index included below is an alphabetical listing of the first line of each verse that appears in the present work, the *Akṣara-puruṣottama-darśana-kārikā-sañcaya*. Every entry is accompanied by its verse number as it appears in this book (indicated by Sa.No.), the corresponding kārikā number from the *Siddhanta-sudhā* (indicated by Kā.No.), and page number as it appears in this work (indicated by Pg.). This tool is intended to 1) help students of the *Siddhanta-sudhā* locate the translations and other tools offered in this book and 2) assist this book's readers in accessing the *Siddhanta-sudhā's* detailed explanations and contextualisation of each verse.

Verse	Sa.No.	Kā.No.	Pg.
akārtsnyaṃ vaiparītyaṃ ca tathaiva saṃśayādikam	90	230	103
akṣaraṃ brahma vijñeyaṃ mantre svāmīti śabdataḥ	28	2	32
ataḥ śāstrā''śrayo śreyān anumānādalaukike	110	270	123
ato'rthāpattirityādeścet siddhāntā'virodhitā	114	275	127
atyantamasamartho'pi brahmaṇaḥ parabrahmaṇaḥ	137	348	159
anādikālataḥ sarvamāyikopādhivarjitaḥ	15	–	19
anādyajñānarūpeyaṃ vikṣepamohakāriṇī	121	281	137
anu hetumitiṃ nityaṃ sādhyasya jāyate mitiḥ	96	245	109
anumānaṃ dvidhaṃ proktaṃ svārthaparārthabheda	97	250	110
ayaṃ bhāgavato dharmaḥ sambandhāducyate hareḥ	149	388	176
aśnotervyāpanārthāddhi nañpūrvātkṣaratestathā	38	16	46
asmāddhi sutarāṃ nyūnā dharmā varṇā''śramocitāḥ	150	389	177
ahamātmā'smyahaṃ brahma brahmarūpe mayi	155	402	182
ājñā harerguroścaiva sadācārādirūpiṇī	152	391	179
ājñopāsanasadbhāvapakṣā hi jīvajīvanam	142	–	169
ātmā jñānā'vinābhāvī jñānamātravihīnatām	91	234	104
ātmā'ntaḥkaraṇā''ḍhyaṃ syāt pramāṇaṃ cakṣurādi	95	244	108

Verse	Sa.No.	Kā.No.	Pg.
ādau bhaktyaṅgajanmā gahanavanagatirnīlakaṇṭha	2	–	4
icchājñānakriyāśakterjīvānāṃ yaḥ pradāyakaḥ	125	–	145
icchāśaktiḥ parāllabdhā jñānaśaktistathaiva ca	131	334	151
itihāsapurāṇābhyāṃ tasmāt tadupabṛṃhaṇam	104	258	117
indriyasaṃyamo māyāvikārādividāraṇam	161	418	188
utpattiśca sthitiścaiva pralayaśceti yat trayam	140	351	162
utsāho'bhyasanaṃ dhairyaṃ viśvāsaḥ saṃyamo	165	422	191
upādānaṃ nimittaṃ ca kāraṇaṃ jagato mataḥ	66	172	76
upādānaṃ nimittaṃ ca taddhi sarjanakāraṇam	43	22	51
ekamevākṣaraṃ brahma mokṣopāyatayā dhruvam	164	421	190
etaddehatrayād bhinno jīvātmā'yaṃ sanātanaḥ	128	326	148
etāni sādhanāni syurguruprasannatā yataḥ	167	424	193
evaṃ dhyātvā tvadājñāyāmanuvṛttau ca vartanam	23	–	27
aiśvaryaṃ sarvamuktānāṃ sarvajñatvādilakṣaṇam	177	456	206
aiśvaryādīśvaraḥ prokto jīvād bhinnaḥ svarūpataḥ	136	347	158
kalyāṇaṃ paramaṃ bhūyānnaikajīveśvarā''tmanām	73	198	83
kevalamanumānaṃ tu parātmasādhakaṃ na hi	109	269	122
kolāhalaśca kalahaśca kukarmaghātāḥ	6	–	10
guṇātītaṃ guruṃ prāpya brahma rūpaṃ nijātmanaḥ	33	–	41
guṇānetānatītya trīn sādharmyaṃ brahmaṇā bhavet	124	291	140
gururakṣarabrahmaiva divyo divyatanordharaḥ	53	67	61
gurureva mama dhyānaṃ vyākhyānaṃ me guruḥ	25	–	29
gurulābhā'mṛtaṃ sākṣād haraye gurave tathā	181	–	210
guruharibalaṃ śreṣṭhaṃ śāstravacobalādapi	112	272	125
gurorjñānamiva jñānaṃ vartanamapi tatsamam	146	369	173
caturdhā'vasthitirjñeyā kāryabhedānna tattvataḥ	44	40	52
cidākāśastathā deśastaddeśasthaśca sevakaḥ	45	41	53

Verse	Sa.No.	Kā.No.	Pg.
chāndogye daharā''kāśaścidākāśaḥ prakīrtitaḥ	46	43	54
janma karma sadā divyamakṣarādhipateryathā	58	74	66
janma nāsti mṛtirnāsti nitya ātmā sanātanaḥ	132	340	152
jāgaraṇaṃ tathā svapnaḥ suṣuptiśceti budhyate	129	329	149
jīvayati svadehaṃ yo jīvati ca svayaṃ yataḥ	126	314	146
jīvastatheśvaro māyā brahma paramabrahma ca	29	3	33
jīvātmā nityaśuddho'sti māyāmalavivarjitaḥ	135	345	155
jñānaṃ pramātmakaṃ jñeyaṃ yathā'vasthitavastu	89	229	102
jñānayajñamayo nityaṃ śrīharyājñānupālakaḥ	18	–	22
tato bhinne tu citkhyātirvaiparītyaṃ yadā bhavet	117	278	130
tatparaḥ paramātmā'sti parabrahmeti śabditaḥ	40	18	48
tatrā'pi mānavākāraḥ kiśoro dvibhujaḥ sadā	76	214	86
tadeva yājñavalkyoktau gārgīpraśnottare sthitam	47	47	55
tasmāddhareḥ svarūpaṃ tu sākārameva sarvadā	77	215	87
tasmāddhi brahmabhāvo'yaṃ samyagiha nirūpyate	144	367	171
tādṛgupaniṣannāsti gītā'dhyāyo na vidyate	59	163	67
tūryā'vasthā sthitirbrāhmī muktirūpā prakīrtitā	130	331	150
te pañca sādhuniyamā nanu pañca divyā	7	–	11
triguṇasāmyavaiṣamye yadādhipatyasambhave	118	–	134
dayārṇavaḥ kṛpāsādhyaḥ prasādāt sulabhā kṛpā	143	366	170
divyaguṇaviśiṣṭo'yaṃ māyikaguṇavarjitaḥ	64	170	74
divyasaṃkalpamātreṇa naikānāmuddidhīrṣayā	69	175	79
divyo divyā'tidivyo'yaṃ svasaṅgād divyatāpradaḥ	84	224	94
divyo'si madguruḥ sākṣāt tvaṃ parabrahmadhārakaḥ	22	–	26
dehapātottaraṃ labhyā videhamuktirucyate	172	437	201
dehastho dehabhinno'yaṃ dehendriyaprakāśakaḥ	133	341	153
dvāveva nityamuktau sto hyakṣarapuruṣottamau	171	430	200

Verse	Sa.No.	Kā.No.	Pg.
dharmo jñānaṃ ca vairāgyaṃ bhaktiścaitaistribhir	148	387	175
nārāyaṇasvarūpatvād dhyeyo brahmā'kṣaraṃ guruḥ	56	70	64
nārāyaṇasvarūpo'yaṃ sākṣād brahmā'kṣaraṃ guruḥ	13	–	17
nāstyaparaḥ paro loko hyasmāddhyakṣaradhāmataḥ	50	58	58
nimagnāḥ sahajānande pragāḍhā''nandasevitāḥ	175	440	204
nirākārādibhāvā''ḍhyā drohanigrahabandhakṛt	78	216	88
niścitya brahmaparabrahmasvarūpatattvaṃ	5	–	9
naikātmanaḥ paramamokṣapathaṃ vinetuṃ	12	–	16
pañcīkāro bhaved yatra satkāryatopapadyate	116	277	129
patravyākhyānarūpo'yaṃ suḍhāgrantho hi kevalam	32	10	36
parabrahmaṇi bhaktiṃ tu brahmabhāvo'pyapekṣate	147	386	174
paramātmasvarūpasya tvaṃ hi niścāyako guruḥ	20	–	24
paramātmā tu tatraiva samyak sadā virājate	54	68	62
paramātmā paraṃ brahma sarveśvareśvaro hariḥ	62	168	72
paramaikāntiko bhaktaḥ sādhuḥ satpuruṣaśca san	163	420	190
paramaikāntiko bhakto divyabhāvarataḥ sadā	17	–	21
parasmād brahmaṇo bhinnaṃ tadekādhīnatāyutam	41	20	49
paropāsanasiddhyarthaṃ brahmabhāvā''ptaye tathā	37	15	45
punarāvartanaṃ naiva labdhamukteḥ kadācana	178	458	207
pratyakṣaṃ dvividhaṃ jñeyaṃ laukikaṃ ca	92	236	105
pratyakṣabhaktirevoktā śreṣṭhā kṛtsnaphalapradā	160	413	187
pratyakṣādipramāṇeṣu śabdastu pramukho bhavet	108	268	121
pratyakṣo'stīti siddhāntaṃ svāminārāyaṇo bhuvi	81	219	91
pratyanīkaṃ bhaved yaddhi pramāyāṃ karaṇaṃ na hi	113	274	126
prāpya navāṃ tanuṃ brāhmīṃ parātmā''kārasaṃ	173	438	202
prārthanā ca mumukṣā ca sahaśca guṇagrāhitā	166	423	192
bāhyendriya'napekṣaṃ yadantaḥ samṛtyādi mānasam	94	239	107

Verse	Sa.No.	Kā.No.	Pg.
brahma mānavarūpeṇa jāyata iti budhyate	57	73	65
brahmaguṇasamāvāptirbhaktaye parabrahmaṇaḥ	145	368	172
brahmaparātmabhinneṣu rāgābhāvo virāgatā	156	407	183
brahmā'kṣarasya divyasya yaddhi yogaṃ vinā bhavet	60	164	67
brahmāsi saccidānando nirvikalpasamādhimān	14	–	18
brahmeśaḥ sahajānandaḥ svayaṃ brahmā'kṣaraṃ	48	49	56
brāhmī sthitiryataḥ siddhyet prākaṭyaṃ parabrahma	34	–	42
bhaktānāṃ brahmarūpāṇāmakṣarapuruṣottamau	176	449	205
bhaktirnānāvidhā proktā śravaṇakīrtanādikā	158	410	185
bhaktistu sahajānande māhātmyajñānabhūṣitā	157	409	184
bhaktereveha prādhānyaṃ dharmādikacatuṣṭaye	151	390	178
bhikṣāṭanaṃ pratidinaṃ prabhurekacchatraṃ	10	–	14
bhrāntau khyātistu vijñeyā cidacitkhyātisaṃjñakā	115	276	128
maṅgalaṃ sahajānandaḥ śrīharirmaṅgalaṃ śubham	1	–	3
manuṣyākāratastaddhi sākṛtikaṃ bhavet sadā	49	55	57
manuṣyādijanerdātā sarvakarmaphalapradaḥ	68	174	78
mahantasvāminaṃ naumi brahmavidyāprabodhakam	26	–	30
mānuṣe divyatāṃ paśyan cintayan varṇayan likhan	85	225	95
māyā triguṇayuktā syād brahmaparātmaśāsitā	119	279	135
māyā'tītaśca nirdoṣaḥ sākṛtirmānavā''kṛtiḥ	63	169	73
māyaiva prakṛtiḥ proktā tamo'ndhakāraśabditā	122	282	138
māhātmyasahitaḥ samyaṅniścayaḥ paramātmanaḥ	162	419	189
muktirhi svātmabrahmaikyapūrvakaṃ dāsabhāvataḥ	169	427	198
mūrtimadbrahmaṇā nityaṃ muktaistadbhāvabhāvi	65	171	75
yatkāruṇyakaṇasparśānmuktiḥ karatalāyate	168	–	197
yatsaṃkalpā'nugaṃ vastubhūtisthityādi sarvadā	86	–	99
yathā brahmagurau vāsaḥ svāminārāyaṇaprabhoḥ	55	69	63

Verse	Sa.No.	Kā.No.	Pg.
yathāvat prabhumāhātmyaṃ dharma ekāntikastathā	21	–	25
yaśca karaṇarūpādernişedhaḥ śrūyate śrutau	75	213	85
yaśca prāmāṇyanirṇetā sarvaprāmāṇyakāraṇam	87	–	100
vacanāmṛtaśāstraṃ hi vārtāśca svāminaḥ śubhāḥ	106	261	119
vārtāmupāsanaparāṃ kurute nitāntaṃ	8	–	12
virāḍatha ca sūtrātmā tṛtīyo'vyākṛtastathā	139	350	161
viśve hyupāsanavidheḥ suvikāsahetor	11	–	15
vedavedāntaśāstreṣu pracchannaṃ gūḍhamakṣaram	35	13	43
śabdeṣu sādhitaṃ yaddhi saprapañcaṃ nirūpitam	182	–	212
śabdo yo hi yathārthaḥ syāt prāmāṇyaṃ bhajate	100	254	113
śāstraśabdo'pi no sevyo gurorāśrayaṇaṃ vinā	111	271	124
śikṣādīnāṃ tadaṅgānāṃ vedarakṣā prayojanam	103	257	116
śuddhabhāvena yo bhakto brahmamantā bhaved	24	–	28
śrīvardhamānapura - bhogavatītaṭasthe	9	–	13
śrīhariḥ sahajānandaḥ svayamupadideśa yam	27	1	31
śrīhariparabhāvajñaḥ sevyo'pi bhagavāniva	19	–	23
śreyo'nantaguṇairyuktaṃ māyādoṣavivarjitam	42	21	50
śvāse śvāse ca satsaṅgaṃ divyamalaukikaṃ śubham	185	–	215
sa eva paramopāsyo bhajanīyaśca bhāvataḥ	71	178	81
sa eva prakaṭo nityaṃ pratyakṣe brahmaṇi gurau	72	179	82
sa eva sahajānandaḥ svāminārāyaṇo hariḥ	70	177	80
saṃhitābrāhmaṇātmā yastathopaniṣadātmakaḥ	102	256	115
sagarāmādayaḥ śreṣṭhā sādhavo dhārmikā matāḥ	154	396	181
sattvaṃ rajastamaśceti trayaḥ syuḥ prakṛterguṇāḥ	123	287	139
satyasiddhāntasarvasvaṃ sahajānandabodhitam	31	9	35
satsaṅgānnādhikaṃ kiñcid guruprasaṅgalakṣaṇāt	184	–	214
sadācārādiniṣṭho yo kvāpi varṇasthito bhavet	153	395	180

Verse	Sa.No.	Kā.No.	Pg.
santuṣṭā dṛḍhaniṣṭhāto hyakṣarapuruṣottame	183	–	213
samyag vāso yatastatra hyudbhūtasarvaśaktikaḥ	83	223	93
sarvakartā samutkṛṣṭaḥ sākṛtiḥ prakaṭaḥ sadā	159	412	186
sarvajīveśvarebhyaśca māyātanmuktatastathā	39	17	47
sarve muktāḥ samā''kārā nyūnā'dhikatvavarjitāḥ	174	439	203
sahajānandasevāyāṃ dhāmni yad rājate sadā	51	60	59
sahitaḥ svāminā nityamāste nārāyaṇo hariḥ	61	–	71
sā punardvividhā proktā brahmasthitimatāṃ dhruvā	170	428	199
sākṛtireva kartā'yaṃ sākṛtirvyāpako mataḥ	74	212	84
sākṣādbrahmasvarūpe prakaṭaguruvare prītikāṣṭhāṃ	141	–	167
sākṣādvedo bhaved vākyaṃ svāminārāyaṇaprabhoḥ	105	260	118
sāpekṣaṃ dvividhaṃ jñeyaṃ bāhyamābhyantaraṃ	93	238	106
siddhāntapuṣpasuphalāmṛtadivyagandhī	4	–	7
siddhāntasaṃgraheṇaivaṃ kārikā racitā imāḥ	179	179	208
siddhāntā'nugamanyattu sarvathā sāmpradāyikam	107	262	120
sisṛkṣuḥ sahajānandaḥ prathamatastadīkṣate	52	62	60
sukhī ca sukharūpo'yaṃ śāstraiḥ parikīrtitaḥ	134	343	154
sṛṣṭyupādānabhūteyaṃ heturanādisaṃsṛteḥ	120	280	136
sevitaḥ sahajānando bhaktaistatkālikairmudā	82	222	92
so'yaṃ śrīsahajānandaḥ sarvopari parātparaḥ	80	218	90
sthitaprajñaḥ paro yogī nivṛtto'si pravartane	16	–	20
sthūlamekaṃ tathā sūkṣmaṃ tṛtīyaṃ kāraṇaṃ	127	322	147
svakarmaphalabhoktā'yaṃ jñeyo'cchedyādilakṣaṇaḥ	138	349	160
svataḥ sarvasamutkṛṣṭaḥ sarvatra sarvathā sadā	79	217	89
svadhāmasthita evā'yaṃ sakalā'nvitatāṃ gataḥ	67	173	77
svāmināradyaṇaṃ naumi hyakṣarapuruṣottamam	3	–	6
svāminārāyaṇaṃ vande hyakṣarapuruṣottamam	88	–	101

Verse	Sa.No.	Kā.No.	Pg.
svāminārāyaṇenaivaṃ padārthāḥ pañca kīrtitāḥ	30	4	34
svāmivārtā'mṛtaṃ divyaṃ divyaṃ ca vacanā'mṛtam	180	–	210
svīyopadeśavārtāsu guṇātītena brahmaṇā	36	14	44
harergurośca yaḥ śabdaḥ pramāṇaṃ nikhilo mataḥ	101	255	114
heturupamiteryaḥ syādupamānaṃ taducyate	99	253	112
hetuvaddhi yadābhāso hetavo dūṣitā matāḥ	98	251	111

Glossary

Abhidhyānam – Worshipful salutation or obeisance.

Acitkhyati – Erroneous knowledge that has as its object that which undergoes quintuplication or satkāryatā.

Ahantva – Ego, or the quality of 'I-ness', that is caused by māyā.

Aiśvarya – Enhanced faculties that often facilitate governance.

Ājñā – Obedience to divine ordinances.

Akṣara – See entry under 'Akṣarabrahman'.

Akṣarabrahman – A sentient being that Parabrahman employs through such processes as genesis, sustenance, and liberation. It is also known as 'Akṣara' and 'Brahman'. It is a singular entity, yet it takes on four forms to fulfil its various service roles: 1) the cidākāśa, which pervades and sustains creation; 2) the divine abode, which houses Parabrahman and the released jīvas and īśvaras; 3) the servant within the divine abode, which acts as an ideal for released jīvas and īśvaras; and 4) the guru, who comes to earth and acts as a vessel through which Parabrahman can manifest and help people secure liberation.

Akṣaradhāman – Parabrahman's divine abode.

Akṣaramukta – A released soul that is of the jīva or īśvara category.

Akṣara-Puruṣottama Darśana – The system of philosophical teachings propounded by Parabrahman Swaminarayan and later coined by Brahmasvarūpa Shastriji Maharaj.

Akṣararūpa – See entry under the term 'brahmarūpa'.

Alaukika – That which is not worldly or corporeal.

Andhakāra – Darkness; also used to describe māyā.

Antaḥkaraṇa – The inner faculties.

Antaryāmin – That which is eternally present within all and governs all.

Anumāna – Inference.

Anupalabdhi – Non-cognition.

Arcimārga – The path that a jīva or īśvara takes on its way to Parabrahman's divine abode.

Anvaya – When used to describe a metaphysical entity, it indicates the entity's pervasiveness. In pedagogy, it refers to a didactic tool that helps in the interpretation of a Saṃskṛta verse. Placing a verse in anvaya order involves rearranging its component parts in grammatical sequence.

Arthāpatti – Postulation.

Aśnoti – A Saṃskṛta verb that denotes pervasiveness.

Āśrama – A common term used to describe the four stages of life, namely, brahmacarya, gṛhastha, vānaprastha, and sannyāsa.

Ātman – The individual soul or self.

Avatāra – An incarnation of God.

Ātmarūpa – See entry under 'brahmarūpa'.

Avatārin – The cause of the incarnations; Parabrahman.

Avyākṛta – One of the īśvara's three bodies.

Bhadreshdas Swami (Bhadreśadāsa Svāmī) – Author of the *Prasthānatrayī-svāminārāyaṇa-bhāṣyam* and the *Svāminārāyaṇa-siddhānta-sudhā*.

Bhagatji Maharaj (Bhagatajī Mahārāja) – Swaminarayan's second spiritual successor, who lived from 1829 to 1897 CE.

Bhagavadgītā – A text of 700 verses that encapsulates a philosophical discussion between Krishna and Arjuna on the brink of the Mahābhārata war. This text forms the smṛti prasthāna (the retrospective component) of the Prasthānatrayī or the texts that comprise the Vedāntic canon.

Bhagavān – One who possesses divine faculties; most often used to refer to the Almighty.

Bhāgavata dharma – See entry under 'ekāntika dharma'.

Bhogāvatī River – A body of water that runs through western and northern Gujarat; it is known colloquially as the Bhogāvo River.

Bochasan – A town in present-day central Gujarat that serves as home to the first traditional, stone mandira dedicated entirely to the Akṣara-Puruṣottama Darśana. This mandira, consecrated in 1907, was the first of five such edifices built by Brahmasvarūpa Shastriji Maharaj.

Brahmabhāva – The state of having attained qualitative oneness with Akṣarabrahman; also known as brahmasthiti and brāhmī sthiti. One who has attained this state is known as being brahmarūpa.

Brahman – See entry under 'Akṣarabrahman'.

Brahmarūpa – The state of having attained cognitive, qualitative oneness with Akṣarabrahman. Also referred to as ātmarūpa and svāmirūpa.

Brahmasūtras – A text of aphorisms created by Vyāsa as a concordance of the Upaniṣads. This text forms the tarka prasthāna (the logical component) of the Prasthānatrayī or the texts that comprise the Vedāntic canon.

Brahmasthiti – See entry under 'brahmabhāva'.

Brahmavidyā – The knowledge of Akṣarabrahman and Parabrahman, or Akṣara and Puruṣottama, according to Muṇḍakopaniṣad 1.2.13.

Brāhmavigraha – A body that is made of the divine element known as Akṣarabrahman. Jīvas and īśvaras receive such a body upon attaining videha-mukti, or the liberation that occurs after death.

Brāhmaṇa – One of the four castes that made up traditional Indian society. Brāhmaṇas were generally charged with studying and teaching the scriptures and officiating sacred rites.

Brāhmī sthiti – See entry under 'brahmabhāva'.

Brāhmī tanu – A body that is made of the divine element known as Akṣarabrahman. Jīvas and īśvaras receive such a body upon attaining videha-mukti, or the liberation that occurs after death.

Brahmasvarūpa guru – Another word for the Akṣarabrahman guru. This guru serves as a vessel for God through whom devotees may attain liberation and interact with the Divine while on earth.

Bṛhadārāṇyaka Upaniṣad – One of the ten principal Upaniṣads.

Cetana – A sentient being, such as the jīvas and īśvaras.

Chāndogya Upaniṣad – One of the ten principal Upaniṣads.

Chapaiyā – A village in northern India that falls in the present-day state of Uttar Pradesh. Parabrahman Bhagwan Swaminarayan took birth in this village in 1781.

Cidākāśa – One of Akṣarabrahman's four forms. The cidākāśa is the pervasive form that sustains creation and governs over all according to Parabrahman's wish. It is also known as the daharākāśa.

Cidacitkhyati – Erroneous knowledge that has as its object that which is not subject to quintuplication or satkāryatā and that which is subject to quintuplication or satkāryatā.

Citkhyati – Erroneous knowledge that has as its object that which is not subject to quintuplication or satkāryatā.

Daharākāśa – See entry under 'cidākāśa'.

Darśana – This term can refer to the act of seeing or to the instrument by which one can see or know. When used as part of the term the Akṣara-Puruṣottama Darśana or in reference to it, the term refers to a particular system of beliefs and practices.

Dārśanika – That which is related to any darśana or system of philosophical beliefs.

Dāsabhāva – The disposition of a servant.

Dhārā – A term used to describe a river or stream. The *Svāminārāyaṇa-siddhānta-sudhā's* chapters are analogously known as dhārās. Through this analogy, the text at large is depicted as an ocean of ambrosia that makes itself available to people through a series of rivers.

Dharma – Righteous action; one of the four components of Ekāntika Dharma.

Divyabhāva – The understanding that all are divine.

Ekāntika – This term can be used to describe anyone who has attained spiritual realisation, but is also often used to refer specifically to the Akṣarabrahman guru.

Ekāntika dharma – A collective name for the four endeavours of dharma, jñāna, vairāgya, and bhakti; also referred to as bhāgavata dharma.

Gadhada – A town in present-day, western Gujarat in which Swaminarayan primarily resided during his 25 years of ministry in the state. Of the Vacanāmṛta's 262 discourses, 185 were held in this town.

Gārgī – A Vedic philosopher who challenges the sage Yagnavalkya about issues such as the nature of Aksharabrahman at a debate organised by King Janaka, as described in the Bṛhadāraṇyakopaniṣad.

Ghanshyam (Ghanaśyāma) – The childhood name of Bhagwan Swaminarayan.

Guṇa – 'Quality'. It often refers to māyā's three qualities (sattva, rajas, and tamas) either individually or aggregately.

Gunatitanand Swami (Guṇātītānanda Svāmī) – Bhagwan Swaminarayan's first spiritual successor, who lived from 1785 to 1867. Through his provocative ministry, he consolidated the understanding that Swaminarayan was the manifestation of Parabrahman.

Guṇātīta – One who transcends māyā's three qualities, or guṇas.

Guru – A spiritual guide and nurturer who is the manifestation of Akṣarabrahman and serves as a vessel through which God remains ever-present on earth.

Guru-hari – A moniker for the Akṣarabrahman guru. This term, used by Swaminarayan in the Vacanāmṛta, encompasses the Akṣara-Puruṣottama Darśana's teaching that the guru is a vessel for God, who is also known as Hari.

Iṣṭadeva – One's chosen deity.

Īśvara – A category that consists of sentient beings that enjoy divine faculties that are employed for carrying out various tasks related to the creation, sustenance, and destruction of the world. The īśvara is one of the five eternal metaphysical entities. Īśvaras are often referred to as īśvarātmans.

Itihāsa – A category of sacred texts that includes works that recount history. Examples of itihāsa works include the Rāmāyaṇa and the Mahābhārata.

Jaḍacidātmaka – That which includes both the jaḍa, or unsentient, and cit, or sentient.

Jay Swaminarayan (Jaya Svāminārāyaṇa) – A salutation that is used by members of the Swaminarayan fellowship.

Jīva – The individual soul, which is also referred to as the jīvātman or the ātman. It is one of the five eternal metaphysical entities. Jīvas are individually finite, yet countless in number. They take birth to receive the fruit of their karmas and attain liberation.

Jivan-mukti – Liberation that is experienced while alive.

Jīvātman – See entry under 'jīva'.

Jñāna – Experiential knowledge.

Jñānasvarūpa – That which is inherently sentient.

Jñānayajña – The cognitive practice of identifying oneself with

Akṣarabrahman and offering upāsanā to Parabrahman

Jñātā – That which is the knower.

Kamaṇḍalu – A water pot.

Kārikā – A Saṃskṛta verse that summarises the teachings of a text.

Karma – Action.

Khyāti – Although this term literally refers to knowledge, it is used in Indian epistemology to describe knowledge that is delusional.

Kīrtana – A devotional song or the singing of such a song.

Kṣarati – A Saṃskṛta verb that denotes the act of decay.

Laukika – That which is of this world or corporeal.

Mahant Swami Maharaj (Mahanta Svāmī Mahārāja) – Swaminarayan's sixth spiritual successor and the manifest, Akṣarabrahman guru. He was born in 1933 CE.

Mandira – A house of worship.

Mantra – A word, sentence, or sound that is recited for concentration and prayer.

Mahāpuruṣa – A moniker for the Akṣarabrahman guru.

Mālā – A rosary.

Mamatva – Possessiveness, or the quality of 'my-ness', that is caused by māyā.

Maṅgalācaraṇa – A benedictory verse that appears at the beginning of a treatise. Such verses can also appear in the middle and end of a treatise.

Māyā – The force that shrouds jīvas and īśvaras, preventing them from attaining liberation. Māyā is one of the five eternal metaphysical entities, yet it is the only one that is not sentient. It is formed by three guṇas, or qualities – sattva, rajas, and tamas – and constitutes the base substance from which the material world is created. It is dependent upon and controlled by Parabrahman.

Māyika – That which is somehow related to or born of māyā.

Mukti – Ultimate liberation.

Mumukṣu – 'One who desires liberation'; a spiritual seeker.

Mundakopanishad – One of the ten principal Upaniṣads.

Mūrtimān – That which possesses a definite form.

Nārāyaṇa – Often used as a moniker for Parabrahman; as part of the Swaminarayan mantra, it refers to the historical personality of Bhagwan Swaminarayan.

Narayanswarupdas (Nārāyaṇasvarūpadāsa) – Pramukh Swami Maharaj's name upon initiation.

Neelkanth (Nīlakaṇṭha) – A moniker for Bhagwan Swaminarayan, who was known by this name as a teenage yogī.

Nirdoṣa-buddhi – The understanding of something as being free of flaws arising from māyā.

Nirguṇa – A term used to describe that which is free of māyic qualities or that which is subtle.

Nirlobha – Abstinence from greed; a vow of absolute poverty. It is one of the five principal vows given to ascetics of the Swaminarayan fellowship.

Nirmāna – Humility. It is one of the five principal vows given to ascetics of the Swaminarayan fellowship.

Nirvikalpa – That which involves no doubts. It is often used in the term 'uttama nirvikalpa niścaya', which is the highest form of faith, or nirvikalpa samādhi (a state of realisation in which one exclusively experiences God's bliss).

Niṣkāma – Celibacy. It is one of the five principal vows given to ascetics of the Swaminarayan fellowship.

Nissneha – Non-attachment. It is one of the five principal vows given to ascetics of the Swaminarayan fellowship.

Nissvāda – Detachment from the sense of taste. It is one of the five principal vows given to ascetics of the Swaminarayan fellowship.

Padaccheda – A didactic tool that helps in the interpretation of a Saṃskṛta verse. A verse's padaccheda involves eliminating elisions so that words appear in their original state.

Parabrahman – The greatest sentient being; also known as Puruṣottama and Paramātman.

Parama Ekāntika Bhakta – Another name for the Akṣarabrahman guru.

Paramātman – The greatest sentient being; also known as Puruṣottama and Parabrahman.

Parārtha – That which is for others. This term is often used to describe inference that is performed for the edification of someone other than oneself.

Pradhāna-puruṣa – An īśvara that is instrumental in the process of creation.

Prakṛti – See entry under 'māyā'.

Pramāṇa – A means of valid knowledge.

Pramukha – The administrative head of an organisation.

Pramukh Swami Maharaj – Swaminarayan's fifth spiritual successor, who lived from 1921 to 2016 CE. He consolidated the Akṣara-Puruṣottama Darśana by inspiring: 1) Historic, scholarly works such as the *Svāminārāyaṇa-bhāṣyam* and *Svāminārāyaṇa-siddhānta-sudhā*, and 2) Ornate, large-scale edifices such as Akshardham in Delhi and the Swaminarayan Mandirs in London, Houston, Chicago, and the birthplaces of his predecessors. Through such works, he facilitated, commemorated, and celebrated the practice of the Akṣara-Puruṣottama Darśana.

Praśnopaniṣad – One of the ten principal Upaniṣads.

Prasthānatrayī – A collective name for the canon of texts that is comprised of the Upaniṣads, *Brahmasūtras*, and *Bhagavadgita.*

Pratyakṣa – That which is manifest. When discussing the means of obtaining valid knowledge, or the pramāṇas, pratyakṣa refers to perception.

Purāṇa – A category of sacred texts that encompasses the Bhāgavata Purāṇa, Skanda Purāṇa, Viṣṇu Purāṇa, and other works written by Vyāsa in order to transmit the knowledge of the Vedas to laypersons.

Puruṣa – A sentient being.

Puruṣottama – The greatest sentient being; also known as Parabrahman and Paramātman.

Rajas – One of māyā's three qualities, or guṇas.

Śabda – Verbal testimony; understood as the primary means for gaining knowledge of metaphysical beings and objects.

Sadguru – A senior monk.

Sādhana – Spiritual praxis.

Sādhu – A monk or ascetic.

Saguṇa – A term used to describe that which possessive redemptive qualities or is pervasive.

Sahajanand (Sahajānanda) – A moniker for Bhagwan Swaminarayan.

Sākāra – A term used to describe that which possesses a distinct form.

Sampradāya – A religious fellowship.

Sampradāyika – That which relates to a particular religious fellowship.

Saṃsāra – 'The world'. This term is also often used to refer to the transmigratory cycle or the cycle of births and deaths.

Sansthā – A formally established organisation. It is often used to refer to the Bochasanwasi Akṣara-Puruṣottama Swaminarayan Sanstha, which Brahmasvarūpa Shastriji Maharaj established to propagate the Akṣara-Puruṣottama Darśana.

Sarangpur – A village in present-day western Gujarat that Swaminarayan often visited during his ministry. Eighteen of the Vacanāmṛta's 262 discourses were held in this village.

Śarīrin – That which inhabits something and acts as its controller.

Śāstra – A sacred text.

Satkāryatā – The principle that an effect in the form of a material object necessarily exists within its cause.

Satpuruṣa – Another name for the Akṣarabrahman guru.

Satsaṅga – Association with the Akṣarabrahman guru.

Sattva – One of māyā's three qualities, or guṇas.

Shastriji Maharaj (Śāstrijī Mahārāja) – Bhagwan Swaminarayan's third spiritual successor; also known as Yagnapurushdas. He lived from 1865 to 1951 CE. During these years, he coined the term 'Akṣara-Puruṣottama Darśana', consecrated Akṣara-Puruṣottama mūrtis in five exquisite, stone mandiras, and established the Bochasanwasi Akṣara-Puruṣottama Swaminarayan Sanstha (BAPS), an organisation meant to facilitate the propagation of the Akṣara-Puruṣottama Darśana.

Shri Hari (Śrī Hari) – A moniker for Bhagwan Swaminarayan.

Siddhānta – A philosophical principle.

Siddhānta-patram – A philosophical document written by Pramukh Swami Maharaj in 2008 encompassing Bhagwan Swaminarayan's Akṣara-Puruṣottama Darśana.

Śikṣā – One of the six Vedic aṅgas, or fields of inquiry that one must master before embarking on Vedic study.

Śravaṇa – 'Listening'. It is one of the principal types of bhakti and primarily encompasses listening to discourses.

Śruti – 'That which is heard'. This term most often refers to the Vedas, which encompass the Upaniṣads. It is also used as a general term to refer to individual verses from these texts.

Sthitaprajña yogī – A practitioner of yoga who has attained complete stability of mind and is focused on worshipping Paramātman.

Sudhā – Ambrosia. It is used at times as a concise way of referring to the *Svāminārāyaṇa-siddhānta-sudhā.*

Śūdra – One of the four castes that made up traditional Indian society.

Sūtrātmā – One of the īśvara's three bodies.

Svabhāva – One's inherent nature.

Svāmi – Often used as a respectful title for initiated monks in the Swaminarayan fellowship. As part of the Swaminarayan mantra, it refers to the historical personality of Akṣarabrahman Gunatitanand Swami.

Svāmīnī Vāto – A textual compilation of Akṣarabrahman Gunatitanand Swami's discourses.

Svāmirūpa – See entry under 'brahmarūpa'.

Svāmi-sevakabhāva – The disposition that a servant holds towards their master.

Swaminarayan (Svāminārāyaṇa) – The manifest form of Parabrahman and the original teacher of the Akṣara-Puruṣottama Darśana. He lived from 1781 to 1830 CE and remains ever present on earth-through a lineage of Akṣarabrahman gurus. See introduction for more information.

Swaminarayan mantra (Svāminārāyaṇa mantra) – The mantra chanted by all followers of the Swaminarayan fellowship. In this mantra, 'Svāmī' refers to the Akṣarabrahman guru, and 'Nārāyaṇa' refers to Parabrahman. Embedded in the recitation of this mantra is the cognitive act of identifying with Akṣarabrahman and worshipping Parabrahman.

Svāminārāyaṇa-siddhānta-sudhā – A didactic, Saṃskṛta treatise written by Sadhu Bhadreshdas in 2017 that offers a systematic and comprehensive exposition, justification and defence of the Akṣara-Puruṣottama Darśana's theological and philosophical principles.

Svārtha – That which is done for oneself. This term is often used to describe a particular type of inference, namely, that which is performed for one's own knowledge.

Tamas – One of māyā's three qualities.

Upamāna – Analogy.

Upaniṣad – A category of texts that form part of the Vedas. Along with the Vedas in general, these texts are also known as the śrutis (that which is heard), as they were initially revealed to enlightened ṛṣis, who heard them and transmitted them to their disciples. These texts are also known as the Vedānta, as they represent the philosophical essence of the Vedas. For centuries, ten Upaniṣads particular have been understood to represent the śruti prasthāna (revelatory component) of the Prasthānatrayī or the texts that comprise the Vedāntic canon.

Upāsanā – Faithful worship.

Uttama nirvikalpa niścaya – The highest form of conviction in God. It is described in Vacanāmṛta L-12 as the state of worshipping God upon having attained qualitative oneness with Akṣarabrahman.

Uttar Pradesh – A state in northern India.

Vacanāmṛta – A text that contains compiled discourses from Swaminarayan ministry. This work was composed in Swaminarayan's presence and contains Swaminarayan's original teachings of the Akṣara-Puruṣottama Darśana.

Vāda-grantha – A didactic, Saṃskṛta treatise that offers a systematic and comprehensive exposition, justification and defence of a school of thought's theological and philosophical principles.

Vadhvan - See entry under 'Vardhamana'.

Vairāgya – Detachment. It is one of the four endeavours that comprise ekāntika dharma.

Vandanā – Worshipful salutation or obeisance.

Varṇa – Caste.

Vardhamana – A village in present-day, western Gujarat that is commonly known as Vadhvan. This village served home to the first traditional mandira in which the mūrtis of Akṣara and Puruṣottama were enshrined.

Vartal – See entry under 'Vruttalaya'.

Vāsanā – Desire.

Vasanta – The Indian spring season.

Vasanta-tilakā – A metre in Saṃskṛta verse.

Veda – Sacred texts that comprise the core of Indian religious literature. The Veda is divided into four parts: 1) the Ṛg Veda, 2) the Yajur Veda, 3) the Sāma Veda, and 4) the Atharva Veda. Each of these parts, in turn, has four sections: 1) the Saṃhitās, 2) the Brāhmaṇas, 3) the Āraṇyakas, and 4) the Upaniṣads. The Vedas and its parts are all known as 'śruti' (that which is heard), as they were initially revealed to ṛṣis, who heard them and passed them on to their disciples.

Vedic – That which relates to the Vedas.

Videha-mukti – The form of liberation that occurs after death.

Virāt Puruṣa – The īśvara that presides over a brahmāṇḍa, or unit of creation. This entity is also known as Virāṭ.

Vruttalaya – A village in present-day, central Gujarat that Swaminarayan often visited during his ministry. Twenty of the Vacanāmṛta's 262 discourses were held in this village.

Vyatireka – Distinct or separate. When used to describe Parabrahman, this term refers to the human form of God that resides in the divine abode.

Yagnapurushdas (Yajñapuruṣadāsa) – See entry under 'Shastriji Maharaj'.

Yajña – A fire ritual in which offerings are made to God.

Yājñavalkya – A ṛṣi who answers Gārgī's questions about Akṣarabrahman and other topics during King Janaka's yajña, as described in the Bṛhadāraṇyakopaniṣad.

Yogiji Maharaj (Yogījī Mahārāja) – Bhagwan Swaminarayan's fourth spiritual successor. He lived from 1892 to 1971, during which he spread the Akṣara-Puruṣottama Darśana outside of India, established regular assemblies and publications for teaching the darśana, and initiated formally educated youths as sadhus.

Yogī – An ascetic who practices yoga.

Works Cited

Bhadreshdas, Sadhu. *Brahmasūtra-Svāminārāyaṇa-Bhāśyaṃ*. Swaminarayan Aksharpith, 2009.

---. *Śrīmad-Bhagavadgītā-Svāminārāyaṇa-Bhāṣyam*. Swaminarayan Aksharpith, 2012.

---. *Svāminārāyaṇa-Siddhānta-Sudhā*. Swaminarayan Aksharpith, 2017.

---. *Upaniṣat-Svāminārāyaṇa-Bhāṣyam*, Vol.1. Swaminarayan Aksharpith, 2009.

---. *Upaniṣat-Svāminārāyaṇa-Bhāṣyam*, Vol.2. Swaminarayan Aksharpith, 2012.

---. *Upaniṣat-Svāminārāyaṇa-Bhāṣyam*, Vol.3. Swaminarayan Aksharpith, 2012.

Dave, Harshadray. *Bhagavān Śrī Svāminārāyaṇa*. 4th ed., vol. 1–5, Swaminarayan Aksharpith, 2004.

---. *Brahmasvarūpa Śāstrījī Mahārāj*. 3rd ed., vol. 1–2, Swaminarayan Aksharpith, 1995.

Gōvindācārya. *Vaiyākaraṇasiddhāntakaumudī (Aṣṭādhyāyīsūtrapāṭha-Vārtikapāṭha-Gaṇapāṭha-Dhātupāṭha-Pāṇinīyaśikṣā-Liṅgānuśāsana-Paribhāṣāpāṭha-Sūtravārtikagaṇasūtradhātuparibhāṣōṇādisūtrānukramaṇikāsaṁvalitā) (Mūlamātram)*. Chaukhamba Surabharati Prakashan.

Jha, Naresh, editor. Mahāmuni-Pāṇinipraṇītaḥ Dhātupāṭhaḥ (Sārthaḥ Saprayogaśca). Chaukhamba Surabharati Prakashan.

Sāyaṇācārya. Mādhavīyadhātuvṛttiḥ. Edited by Sadāśivaśāstrī, Chaukhambha, 2010.

Swaminarayan, Bhagwan. *Vacanāmṛta*. Edited by Swami Muktanand et al., Swaminarayan Aksharpith, 2013.